THE HEALTH OF THE NATION

A STRATEGY FOR

HEALTH IN ENGLAND

Presented to Parliament

by the Secretary of State for Health

by Command of Her Majesty July 1992

Reprinted 1993
(with corrections)

Cm 1986   **LONDON: HMSO**   **PRICE £13.60 net**

CONTENTS

INTRODUCTION BY THE SECRETARY OF STATE FOR HEALTH

"The Health of the Nation" Green Paper, published in June 1991, stimulated an extensive public debate. More than 2,000 individuals and organisations sent in their views. Dozens of conferences, seminars and workshops were held. Newspaper and journal articles were written debating the issues raised.

Of course, many different views were expressed. But one thing above all was apparent: the very wide backing which the overall strategy set out in the Green Paper attracted. There was support for the need to concentrate on health promotion as much as health care; for the need to set clear and challenging targets – and not too many of them – at which to aim; and for the need for all of us to work together. These principles are essential if we are to make further significant improvements in the health of the people. The consultation showed that the time is right for the development of a strategic approach to health. It also confirmed the opportunities which exist.

The quality of the debate has revealed a common perception of what needs to be done. It has exposed the commitment which exists to make sure this is achieved. We are well placed to meet the targets set in this White Paper. If we succeed, the health of the nation will be substantially improved.

The Green Paper acknowledged our debt to the World Health Organisation's "Health For All" strategy. I was particularly heartened by the warm welcome which WHO gave to our Green Paper. Now we will build on this, in a way designed to meet the particular circumstances in this country.

The priorities, the targets, the mechanisms and the action set out in this document speak for themselves. I should, however, like to emphasise four points.

> **First**, there is a commitment in this White Paper to the pursuit of 'health' in its widest sense, both within Government and beyond. Within Government

this reflects not only my role as Secretary of State for Health but also the responsibilities of my colleagues in other Departments.

Second, the reforms of the NHS have made this strategic approach possible. The need to focus on health as much as health care has long been the ambition. The reforms have enabled us to make it a reality.

Third, although there is much that Government and the NHS need to do, the objectives and targets cannot be delivered by Government and the NHS alone. They are truly for the nation – for all of us – to achieve. We must be clear about where responsibilities lie. We must get the balance right between what the Government, and Government alone, can do, what other organisations and agencies need to do and, finally, what individuals and families themselves must contribute if the strategy is to succeed.

Fourth, this White Paper is not the last word. It is only the start of a continuing process of identifying priority objectives, setting targets and monitoring and reviewing progress. Over time new objectives and targets will be set, adding to or replacing those in this White Paper.

This initiative is unique. It builds on achievements, both past and present. It proposes action and provides the focus for that action. Its ultimate purpose is to bring about further continuing improvement in the health of the nation.

Virginia Bottomley
Secretary of State for Health
Whitehall
LONDON

July 1992

SUMMARY OF THE STRATEGY FOR HEALTH

The aim of the consultative document "The Health of the Nation" was to stimulate a period of widespread public and professional debate on health and how it might be improved. This White Paper sets out a strategy for health for England which takes account of the response to consultation. The strategy

- selects five Key Areas for action
- sets national objectives and targets in the Key Areas
- indicates the action needed to achieve the targets
- outlines initiatives to help implement the strategy
- sets the framework for monitoring, development and review.

THE STRATEGIC APPROACH

The strategy is set against the background of a continuing overall improvement in England's general state of health *(chapter 1)*. It emphasises disease prevention and health promotion as ways in which even greater improvements in health can be secured, while acknowledging that further improvement of treatment, care and rehabilitation remains essential.

KEY AREAS FOR ACTION AND NATIONAL TARGETS

Five Key Areas, in which substantial improvement in health can be achieved, are selected *(chapter 2)*. Each Key Area has national targets, and is supported by action needed to secure progress. In the main, the targets relate to the year 2000, but some look further to the future. Within Key Areas, emphasis is placed on risk factors, such as smoking or dietary imbalances.

The Key Areas, discussed in detail in the *appendix,* are:

- Coronary heart disease and stroke
- Cancers
- Mental illness
- HIV/AIDS and sexual health
- Accidents.

WORKING TO TAKE THE STRATEGY FORWARD

Everyone has a part to play if the strategy is to be successful. At national level the Government has set up a Ministerial Cabinet Committee to co-ordinate Government action and oversee implementation of the health strategy *(chapter 3)*. Others with major roles include the NHS and health professions, statutory and other authorities, the Health Education Authority, voluntary bodies, employers and employees, and the media.

Chapter 3 also highlights the importance of active partnerships between the many organisations and individuals who can come together to help improve health ("healthy alliances"). Action on a wide variety of fronts will include work in "settings" such as healthy cities, healthy schools or healthy hospitals, specific action on general health promotion in the workplace and of the environment at large.

THE PARTICULAR ROLE OF THE NHS

The NHS has a particularly important role in improving health in addition to its responsibilities for health care *(chapter 4)*. Not only will it work towards achieving progress in the national Key Areas, but it will add to them identified local priorities. The success of the strategy will depend to a great extent on the commitment and skills of the health professionals within the NHS.

MONITORING, DEVELOPING AND REVIEWING THE STRATEGY

The strategy must be monitored and the tools to do so developed. A range of action to meet information and research needs, including major new health survey work, is put in hand *(chapter 5)*. Monitoring and reviewing progress will be overseen by the Ministerial Committee on Health Strategy, assisted by the three Working Groups set up at the start of the initiative. Periodic progress reports will be published.

1

HEALTH IN ENGLAND TODAY

**How health has improved in England – Increased life expectancy –
Today's challenges**

1.1 Health in England is better than it has ever been. Many diseases have been brought under control, and some almost eliminated.

1.2 A century ago four out of ten babies did not survive to adulthood. Life expectancy at birth was only 44 years for boys and 48 for girls. As recently as the early 1930s, 2,500 women a year died during pregnancy or childbirth. The transformation has been profound, as is illustrated in *figures 1* and *2*. Infant

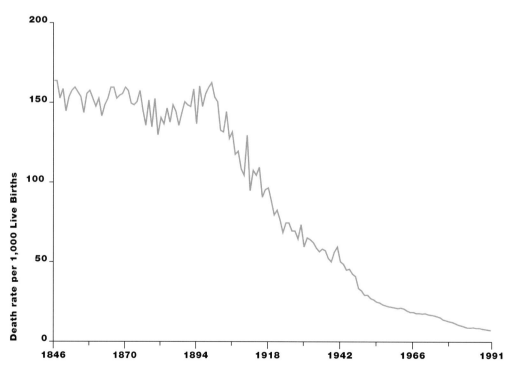

Infant Mortality*   *Figure 1*
England and Wales 1846-1991

Source: OPCS

***Deaths in the first year of life**

6

Figure 2

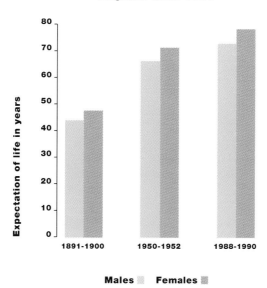

Expectation of Life at Birth
England and Wales 1891 to 1952
England 1988-1990

Source:Government Actuary's Department

mortality, a basic indicator of any nation's health, now stands at under 8 per 1,000 live births. Life expectancy at birth is now 73 years for boys and 79 years for girls.

1.3 Over the last century death rates from infectious diseases have fallen dramatically. For example, tuberculosis has declined steadily over the last 100 years, as is shown in *figure 3*.

1.4 Although immunisation and the development of effective treatments have played their part, this transformation has essentially resulted from social and public health measures.

● Social and public health measures

The provision of safe water and sewerage systems, better living and working conditions, greater economic prosperity, better nutrition and better education have all contributed to these improvements in health.

Figure 3

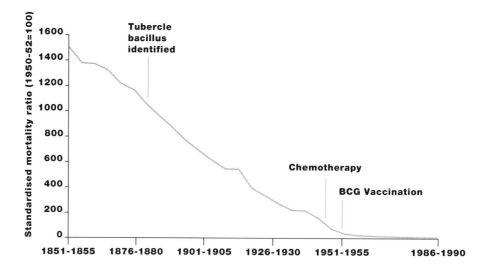

Death rates for Tuberculosis*

England and Wales 1851 to 1990

Source: OPCS (ICD 010:018, 137) after McKeown

*All forms

● Immunisation

A steep decline in polio notifications followed the introduction of polio vaccination, as is shown in *figure 4*. The decline in measles notifications which followed the introduction of the combined measles, mumps and rubella vaccine (MMR) in 1988 represents a more recent success. Mumps has now also been virtually eliminated and rubella infections in pregnancy are very rare.

● Treatment

The introduction of antibiotics in the mid 1940s has had a major impact on mortality from infectious diseases. Other new types of drugs have also contributed to reducing the burden of disease, including drugs for treating hypertension and peptic ulcers. Modern treatment of childhood leukaemia has significantly increased survival and an increased understanding of perinatal physiology has markedly improved the outlook for premature babies. The

Figure 4

Poliomyelitis Notifications
England and Wales 1912-1989

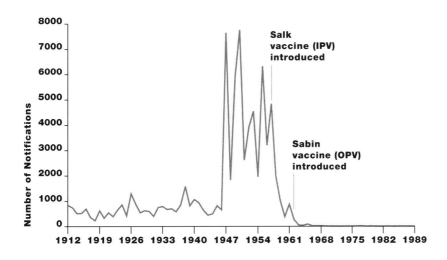

Source: Registrar General; Chief Medical Officer Annual Reports; OPCS MB2 Series

development of new anaesthetic agents and techniques have facilitated dramatic improvements in surgical treatment. More people, particularly elderly people, are able to benefit from surgical interventions such as cataract extraction. Many congenital anomalies can now be corrected. Other major advances in surgery include the development of joint replacement, organ transplantation and microsurgical techniques.

1.5 People may be living longer but many still die prematurely[1] (before age 65) or have the quality of their lives – especially in their later years – impaired by avoidable ill-health. *Figure 5* demonstrates that the contribution of infectious diseases to mortality relative to chronic degenerative diseases – such as the

---

[1] The definition of premature death as death before the age of 65 is a convention used by many countries. It provides a common statistical basis; its use in this document is not to be taken as meaning that deaths after age 65 may not also be premature.

Figure 5

Major causes of death 1931 and 1991*
All persons   England and Wales

1931
(100% = 491,630 deaths)

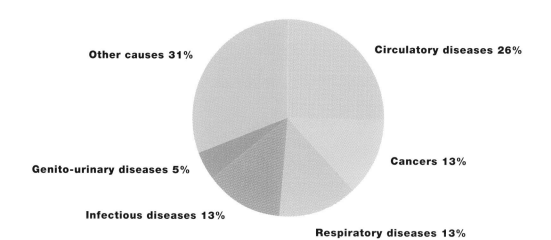

Other causes 31%

Circulatory diseases 26%

Genito-urinary diseases 5%

Cancers 13%

Infectious diseases 13%

Respiratory diseases 13%

1991
(100% = 566,992 deaths)

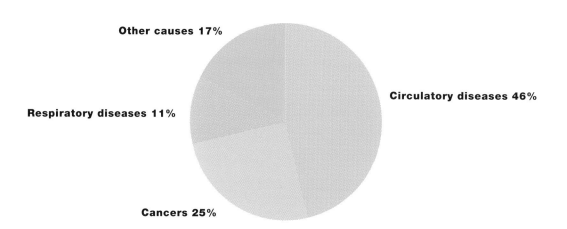

Other causes 17%

Respiratory diseases 11%

Circulatory diseases 46%

Cancers 25%

Source: Registrar General's Statistical Review 1931 and OPCS 1991

*Data for 1991 exclude deaths of those aged under 28 days   **Percentages do not add up to 100 due to rounding**

circulatory diseases, which include coronary heart disease (CHD) and stroke, and cancers – have diminished greatly over time. HIV infection and AIDS pose new challenges. There are also significant variations in ill-health in England as in other countries. The pattern of illness experienced varies in different ethnic, social and occupational groups, and in different geographical regions.

1.6 As has been the case over the last century, today's health problems will need to be tackled on several fronts:

- **Action to promote health and to prevent illness**

  Many people die prematurely or suffer debilitating ill-health from conditions which are to a large extent preventable. The way in which people live and the lifestyles they adopt can have profound effects on subsequent health. Health education initiatives should continue to ensure that individuals are able to exercise informed choice when selecting the lifestyles which they adopt. An increasing number of screening programmes are being implemented, such as those for breast and cervical cancer. The promotion of high uptake rates through effective health education is essential to the success of these programmes. Over the next decade, gains in health will increasingly depend on effective preventive interventions.

- **Improvement in diagnosis, treatment, and rehabilitation**

  Although advances in diagnosis and treatment have already brought about major benefits to health, there is still scope for further developments, both in terms of improving the standards of existing techniques and developing new ones. It will also be important to maintain the quality of care and support provided for chronically sick people, elderly people, mentally ill and handicapped people, and those who are dying. It is essential that there is an appropriate balance between prevention, treatment, and rehabilitation, all of which should aim to improve the quality, as well as the quantity, of life.

- **Environmental quality**

  The environments in which people live and work can have both favourable and adverse effects on their health and well-being. Continued vigilance is needed to maintain the improvements in the environment achieved over the last 150 years and to identify new areas for action. Individuals have little control over many of the threats posed by the external world. It is therefore the responsibility of Government and others to take effective action on behalf of the community as a whole. This is the major theme of the charter on environment and health drawn up by the Office of the European Region of the World Health Organisation. The Charter was reflected in the Government's White paper on the environment "This Common Inheritance" published in September 1990, and the follow-up "Anniversary Report" published a year later in September 1991. Successive annual reports on the environment will develop this theme further, and strengthen the link between further environmental improvements and the health benefits they should help to achieve.

1.7 Today's health problems therefore set new challenges. This White Paper sets out proposals for taking forward a health strategy for England which will meet these challenges.

2

THE STRATEGY FOR HEALTH

The overall goal – Emphasis on health – Strategy based on priority areas where there is greatest need and scope for improvement – The central place of targets – A rolling programme – The first five Key Areas and the targets

2.1 The Government's overall goal is to secure continuing improvement in the general health of the population of England by:

adding years to life: an increase in life expectancy and reduction in premature death; and

adding life to years: increasing years lived free from ill-health, reducing or minimising the adverse effects of illness and disability, promoting healthy lifestyles, physical and social environments and, overall, improving quality of life.

2.2 These concepts are not new. They are an integral part of the World Health Organisation's "Health For All by the Year 2000" approach. The Government acknowledges the important contribution of the "Health For All" approach in the formulation of the strategy for health in England.

2.3 Success will come through, for example:

public policies: by policy-makers at all levels, not only across Government but also in other public bodies and industry, considering the health dimension when developing policies;

healthy surroundings: by the active promotion of physical environments conducive to health – in the home, in schools, at work, on the roads, at leisure, in public places;

healthy lifestyles: by increasing knowledge and understanding about how the way people live affects their health, and enabling families and individuals to act upon this;

high quality health services: by identifying and meeting the health needs of local populations and securing the most appropriate balance between health promotion, disease prevention, treatment, care and rehabilitation.

2.4 Success will also depend on monitoring the population's health, and on research to determine the most effective ways of improving health. This will show how and where resources can be deployed to maximum advantage.

2.5 The need for monitoring and research is especially important in tackling the variations in health between different groups in the population which exist here as in every other country. Effective strategies, whether national or local, will need to be sensitive to these variations, and to focus on the settings in which they are most evident. It will be necessary to identify the variations that occur in particular health problems in order to concentrate efforts on people at particular risk, and to adopt different strategies for different groups. This is discussed further throughout the *appendix*.

2.6 No-one is immortal, but in many cases the onset of illness can be prevented or delayed. When illness strikes, treatment aimed at cure or rehabilitation will continue to be of prime importance. But it is of equal importance to promote good health and well-being, thus preventing illness in the first place. The strategy therefore highlights improving and maintaining **health**, not simply **health care**.

2.7 This strategy is about making the best use of the resources the nation as a whole devotes to health. So far as the Department of Health and the NHS are concerned, it means that decisions about the use of available resources for new initiatives (service or otherwise), research and development and health monitoring should reflect the priorities in this White Paper.

KEY AREAS, OBJECTIVES AND TARGETS

2.8 The Government believes that improvements should, and can, be made in all aspects of health. However, the first step in a strategic approach must be the establishment of clear priorities so that action and resources can be directed to best effect. This is necessary because if everything is regarded as a 'priority' then there is, in effect, no priority at all.

2.9 The Government therefore proposes that the strategy for health should be founded on selected **Key Areas** where there is both the greatest need and greatest scope for making cost-effective improvements in the overall health of the country. For each Key Area, this White Paper sets out the overall **objectives** for improved health, and specific **targets** to be met by set dates. Such targets have a central place in the strategic approach because they clarify what might otherwise be no more than general good intentions. They enable all concerned – whether Government, other bodies or individuals – to focus their efforts on common objectives and provide a yardstick for measuring achievement.

2.10 Three criteria, set out in "The Health of the Nation" Green Paper, governed this first selection of the Key Areas:

- the area should be a major cause of premature death or avoidable ill-health
- effective interventions should be possible, offering significant scope for improvement in health
- it should be possible to set objectives and targets, and monitor progress towards them.

2.11 Key Areas represent the beginning of a rolling programme for priority action. The Green Paper discussed 16 possible areas and many others were suggested in the consultation. A large number were considered, but for a variety of reasons, not all met the criteria. These included:

- areas with existing initiatives which are sufficiently well developed not to require the status of a Key Area, and where the emphasis must be on sustaining and building on progress which has been made already – such as maternal and child health, food safety, oral health, childhood immunisation (for which the Government has set a target of 95% uptake by 1995, the existing target of 90% for all such immunisations having been achieved in May 1992);

- strong candidates for Key Area status where the Government believes that further development and research is necessary before national targets can be set – such as rehabilitation, health of elderly people, asthma, back pain, drug misuse.

2.12 Three other areas discussed in the Green Paper – diabetes, hospital acquired infection (HAI) and breastfeeding – are not selected as Key Areas. They are, nevertheless, important. For example, the Government has asked the Clinical Standards Advisory Group to advise on standards of clinical care for people with diabetes and also to take forward preliminary work on HAI with a view to providing further advice in this area. With regard to diabetes, protocols are already being developed, with the prospect that the targets in the 1989 St Vincent's Declaration (concerned with improving the care and quality of life for people with diabetes) will be achieved as practice improves. In the case of breastfeeding the Government proposes to set up a national working group to help identify and take forward action to increase the proportion of infants breastfed both at birth and at six weeks.

THE INITIAL KEY AREAS

2.13 At the start, the strategy will be based around five priority areas – the Key Areas.

- *Coronary heart disease and stroke* During the consultation there was virtually unanimous agreement that the prevention of coronary heart disease and stroke should be included as a Key Area because of the scope for preventing illness and death from these conditions, and because reductions in risk factors associated with them – unbalanced diet, smoking, raised blood pressure, alcohol misuse and lack of physical activity – would also help to prevent many other diseases.

- *Cancers* The prevention of cancer was selected because of the toll that cancers take in ill-health and death, and because some, but not all, cancers can now be prevented (by actions such as not smoking or avoiding over-exposure to sunlight), and cured as a result of screening and early detection.

- *Mental illness* This was selected because it affects many people and because there is much that can and should be achieved, particularly in relation to improvements in services to reduce the harm that mental illness can cause.

- *HIV/AIDS and sexual health* This was included because it is perhaps the greatest new threat to public health this century. The related areas of *sexual health* and *family planning* are also very important to the health and well-being of individuals and families.

- *Accidents* The prevention of accidents was included because accidents are an important cause of injury, disability and death, particularly in young and elderly people, and can very often be avoided.

2.14 The Key Areas, the objectives and targets which flow from them, and the action needed to secure progress are set out in the following pages. They are discussed in further detail in the *appendix*. Early tasks in all the Key Areas will be to assess further their implications for the use of available resources and to identify the most efficient and effective ways of meeting the targets.

2.15 In framing action within Key Areas the needs of specific groups of people within the population must be considered; the particular needs of children, women, elderly people and people in black and ethnic minority groups and certain socio-economic groups are also considered in the *appendix*.

2.16 Success in these Key Areas would represent a significant improvement in the nation's health in terms of life expectancy, reductions in premature death and improvements in quality of life. Success would also mean resources could be re-deployed to improve services in those areas where, as yet, effective preventive measures are not available.

2.17 The tables set out the "Health of the Nation" targets. The targets are explained fully in the *appendix*.

HEALTH OF THE NATION MAIN TARGETS

Coronary heart disease and stroke[1]

To reduce death rates for both CHD and stroke in people under 65 by at least 40% by the year 2000 *(Baseline 1990)*

To reduce the death rate for CHD in people aged 65–74 by at least 30% by the year 2000 *(Baseline 1990)*

To reduce the death rate for stroke in people aged 65–74 by at least 40% by the year 2000 *(Baseline 1990)*

Cancers[1]

To reduce the death rate for breast cancer in the population invited for screening by at least 25% by the year 2000 *(Baseline 1990)*

To reduce the incidence of invasive cervical cancer by at least 20% by the year 2000 *(Baseline 1986)*

To reduce the death rate for lung cancer under the age of 75 by at least 30% in men and by at least 15% in women by 2010 *(Baseline 1990)*

To halt the year-on-year increase in the incidence of skin cancer by 2005

Mental illness[1]

To improve significantly the health and social functioning of mentally ill people

To reduce the overall suicide rate by at least 15% by the year 2000 *(Baseline 1990)*

To reduce the suicide rate of severely mentally ill people by at least 33% by the year 2000 *(Baseline 1990)*

---

[1] The 1990 baseline for all mortality targets represents an average of three years centred around 1990. See Technical notes on target setting and monitoring, pages 124 – 126.

HIV/AIDS and sexual health

To reduce the incidence of gonorrhoea by at least 20% by 1995 *(Baseline 1990)*, as an indicator of HIV/AIDS trends

To reduce by at least 50% the rate of conceptions amongst the under 16s by the year 2000 *(Baseline 1989)*

Accidents[1]

To reduce the death rate for accidents among children aged under 15 by at least 33% by 2005 *(Baseline 1990)*

To reduce the death rate for accidents among young people aged 15-24 by at least 25% by 2005 *(Baseline 1990)*

To reduce the death rate for accidents among people aged 65 and over by at least 33% by 2005 *(Baseline 1990)*

[1] The 1990 baseline for all mortality targets represents an average of the three years centred around 1990. See Technical notes on target setting and monitoring, pages 124-126.

HEALTH OF THE NATION RISK FACTOR TARGETS

Smoking

To reduce the prevalence of cigarette smoking to no more than 20% by the year 2000 in both men and women (a reduction of a third) *(Baseline 1990)*

To reduce consumption of cigarettes by at least 40% by the year 2000 *(Baseline 1990)*

In addition to the overall reduction in prevalence, at least 33% of women smokers to stop smoking at the start of their pregnancy by the year 2000

To reduce smoking prevalence of 11-15 year olds by at least 33% by 1994 (to less than 6%) *(Baseline 1988)*

Diet and Nutrition

To reduce the average percentage of food energy derived by the population from saturated fatty acids by at least 35% by 2005 (to no more than 11% of food energy) *(Baseline 1990)*

To reduce the average percentage of food energy derived from total fat by the population by at least 12% by 2005 (to no more than about 35% of total food energy) *(Baseline 1990)*

To reduce the proportion of men and women aged 16-64 who are obese by at least 25% and 33% respectively by 2005 (to no more than 6% of men and 8% of women) *(Baseline 1986/87)*

To reduce the proportion of men drinking more than 21 units of alcohol per week and women drinking more than 14 units per week by 30% by 2005 (to 18% of men and 7% of women) *(Baseline 1990)*

Blood Pressure

To reduce mean systolic blood pressure in the adult population by at least 5mm Hg by 2005 *(Baseline to be derived from new national health survey)*

HIV/AIDS

To reduce the percentage of injecting drug misusers who report sharing injecting equipment in the previous 4 weeks from 20% in 1990 to no more than 10% by 1997 and no more than 5% by the year 2000

3

MAKING THE STRATEGY WORK

The Government's role in developing the strategy – Ministerial Cabinet Committee on Health Strategy – Policy development – Individual opportunities – Healthy alliances – Settings for action – Healthy cities, healthy schools, healthy hospitals, healthy homes, healthy workplaces – Healthy environments – The special role of health professionals

3.1 The five Key Areas and their targets set out in the previous chapter are at the centre of the strategy for health. The action needed to reach the targets in each of the Key Areas is set out in the *appendix*.

3.2 Progress towards the targets will also require action *across* Key Areas. This chapter identifies those who have leading roles within and across Key Areas. It highlights, in particular, the significant opportunities offered by joint working and focusing action on various 'settings' – the home, the school, the workplace, cities and the general environment. It also sets out how Government will support and assist these activities and the general development of the strategy.

DEVELOPING THE STRATEGY – THE GOVERNMENT'S ROLE

3.3 The Government is responsible for many elements vital to ensure a healthy population. These responsibilities take a number of forms, including:

- legislation and regulation
- providing reliable information on which individuals can base their decisions on matters which affect their health
- facilitating and encouraging action
- allocating resources
- monitoring and assessing changes in health.

3.4 One of the most important tasks of Government is to ensure that Departments work together towards common objectives. The importance Government attaches to this is demonstrated by the establishment of a

Ministerial Cabinet Committee to oversee implementation, monitoring and development of the English strategy; and to be responsible for ensuring proper co-ordination of UK-wide issues affecting health.

3.5 Membership of the Committee covers 11 Government Departments and it complements existing groups on specific issues such as drugs, alcohol and AIDS.

3.6 The Ministerial Committee will continue to be supported in its work in England by the three Working Groups which were set up following publication of "The Health of the Nation" Green Paper to help with specific aspects of developing and implementing the strategy. These Groups are:

- a "Wider Health Working Group", chaired by the Minister for Health
- a "Health Priorities Working Group", chaired by the Government's Chief Medical Officer
- a "Working Group on Implementation in the NHS", chaired by the Chief Executive of the NHS Management Executive.

DEVELOPING POLICY

3.7 Many policies have, to a greater or lesser degree, an impact on health. It is important, therefore, that as policy is developed the consequences for health are assessed and, where appropriate, taken into account. **The Government will produce guidance on 'policy appraisal and health'** – a similar approach to the guidance on 'policy appraisal and the environment' which was produced following publication of the Environment White Paper "This Common Inheritance".

INDIVIDUAL OPPORTUNITIES AND HEALTHY ALLIANCES

3.8 Everyone has a part to play in improving health, and achieving the targets set out in *chapter 2*. To seize the opportunity, people need information to help make the right choices. Reliable health education in its widest sense is essential for this – pervading education at school and also the many sources of information for people generally about health and its determinants.

3.9 Often the impact on health can be much greater when individuals and organisations work together. Such "healthy alliances" offer a way forward at both local and national level. This approach commanded widespread support during consultation on "The Health of the Nation" Green Paper and many of those responding asked for guidance on forming such healthy alliances. **The Department of Health, with the Wider Health Working Group, will prepare and consult on guidance about the promotion of healthy alliances.**

THE NHS

3.10 One of the key themes of "The Health of the Nation" initiative is that responsibilities for achieving the strategy's objectives and targets go wider than the NHS. Nevertheless, the NHS role as the main provider of health care is crucial to their success. The NHS will need to work with others to initiate and develop common strategies and targets, and to form the healthy alliances needed to take forward action in the Key Areas and other local priorities. The Government looks especially to Regional Health Authorities, working in conjunction with their local health authorities, to initiate the discussion and development of multi-agency approaches to the priorities in this White Paper. The central role of the NHS in the strategy is described more fully in *chapter 4*.

LOCAL AUTHORITIES

3.11 Local authorities have an important role in promoting public health and are key players with health authorities in taking forward the policies in this White Paper. In this context they have two principal responsibilities. They are responsible for protecting the environment in which people live and work. They are also responsible for the purchasing and direct provision of social services to meet the needs of the individual members of the public who live in their area. Environmental Health Departments have a special part to play with their responsibilities for health and safety at work, for food safety and food quality, and in collaboration with health authorities for health promotion and investigating and bringing under control outbreaks of communicable disease. Other environmental regulators, Her Majesty's Inspectorate of Pollution and the Drinking Water Inspectorate, will also have an important role.

3.12 As a result of the NHS reforms and the NHS and Community Care Act local authorities, Family Health Services Authorities and District Health Authorities are working with other agencies to look at the needs of the local population and to match their strategies and policies to those local needs. This is leading both to a greater collaboration than before and joint arrangements about the provision of services across agencies.

3.13 Any of these responsibilities on their own would make the input of local authorities to the strategy for health significant. Taken together the contribution of local authorities is vital. Also, with NHS authorities and others in the community, they can take part in local alliances which can develop initiatives to improve the health of local populations.

THE HEALTH EDUCATION AUTHORITY

3.14 The Health Education Authority (HEA) has well-established national programmes of public health education. It also provides a national stimulus to a wide range of local activity. It works, and will continue to work, closely with the media in delivering accurate health education messages, and with the NHS in developing the health promotion and disease prevention roles of the health service. **The HEA will be reviewing its strategic aims and objectives in the light of the priorities and targets in this White Paper.**

VOLUNTARY ORGANISATIONS

3.15 Voluntary organisations are in a strong position to enhance the health of the population. Between them they cover a broad range of health-related activity. They also have well developed and wide-ranging contacts in, for example, social welfare, sport and recreation, and the environment. More specific roles include:

- through *self-help*, bringing people together to share common problems and to help them gain more confidence and control over their own health;

- by *direct service provision* – voluntary organisations have pioneered a wide variety of services;

- *in community health*, where voluntary organisations work with local people to identify and solve problems affecting their health;

- *health education and promotion, education for health professionals, fund raising and support for research.*

3.16 The Department of Health supports voluntary organisations engaged in health and personal social services work. Funding in 1992/93 is expected to be of the order of £50 million. Much of the work is already concerned with issues set out in this White Paper. Provision for the largest element of the programme – grants under the Section 64 (of the Health Services and Public Health Act 1968) General Scheme – has risen from £15.8 million in 1991/92 to £17.8 million in 1992/93, an increase of 12½%. **The Department of Health has allocated £250,000 in 1992/93 from this increase to fund preliminary voluntary sector work in support of "The Health of the Nation" initiative.**

THE MEDIA

3.17 The media have an important role to play in providing individuals with the information necessary to make decisions which affect their own health and that of their families. People are often confused by the wide variety of sometimes conflicting advice they receive on health matters. It is important therefore that the health messages which people receive from newspapers, magazines, television and radio are accurate, consistent and clear. The Government and the Health Education Authority will play their part by continuing to provide clear and authoritative advice on the factors which can influence health, and on the steps which individuals can take to protect and improve their health.

THE WORKPLACE

3.18 During their working lives, most people spend around a quarter of their time at work. Employers have long been required to provide safe and healthy working conditions. Increasingly they are also recognising the benefits of a workforce with good general health, while trades unions and staff associations are looking for ways to improve the health of their members. The success of the workplace initiative in the Department of Health/Health Education Authority's 'Look After Your Heart' programme demonstrates this growing demand for advice on health and healthy lifestyles. In four years it has been taken up by more than 500 employers covering 3.8 million employees.

ACTION IN DIFFERENT SETTINGS

3.19 "Healthy alliances", either within individual Key Areas or across a number of them, add significantly to the opportunities for progress towards the national targets. Opportunities to work towards the achievement of the targets, and indeed of other health gains, will be similarly enhanced if action – above all joint action – is pursued in various discrete "settings" in the places where people live and work. Such settings include:

- "healthy cities"
- healthy schools
- healthy hospitals
- healthy workplaces
- healthy homes
- healthy environments

They offer between them the potential to involve most people in the country.

HEALTHY CITIES

3.20 A number of cities in England are involved in the WHO 'Healthy Cities' programme. This programme, which started in 1986, now involves 34 European project cities. It seeks to make maximum use of local initiative. Some 75 other towns and cities in England are also involved through the UK Health For All Network – one of 17 such networks throughout Europe. The UK Health For All Network, based in Liverpool, has been supported by the Health Education Authority. The Government is anxious that the Network continues to provide a means of exchanging information amongst participating towns and cities in England and, through WHO, into the wider European network. **The Government will examine ways in which the UK Health For All Network can be further assisted to carry out this work and to increase the number of localities – rural as well as urban – taking part.**

3.21 The Government's action to improve housing recognises the broad link between decent local environment and housing conditions and good health. Housing Action Trusts, Estate Action and the Urban Programme are all designed to promote urban renewal, while City Challenge has stimulated proposals from the competing local authorities to make particularly deprived areas more attractive and healthier places in which to live and work. Alongside this, improvements in local health also depend on local initiative to produce a local equivalent of the national strategy for health – highlighting local health issues and seeking to promote health by involving the people and organisations most directly affected.

HEALTHY SCHOOLS

3.22 An initiative on healthy schools is being developed jointly by WHO, the European Community and the Council of Europe. This will offer opportunities to reach pupils, parents, staff and all who are associated with schools and education. The Government intends that England should play its full part in this initiative and its development. **The Government will seek to establish, jointly with the Health Education Authority and in co-operation with European partners, a pilot network of health promoting schools. This will develop, and assess the effectiveness of, strategies for changing and shaping pupils' patterns of behaviour, with the aim of safeguarding their long-term good health.**

HEALTHY HOSPITALS

3.23 Hospitals exist to provide treatment and care but they also offer unique opportunities for more general health promotion for patients, staff and all who come into contact with them. WHO is currently developing a health promoting hospital initiative. The Government will help with the development of this initiative. **The NHS Management Executive will examine how best the concept of health promoting hospitals can be developed and taken forward from the point of view of patients, public and staff.**

HEALTHY WORKPLACES

3.24 The increasing concern of employers and their workforces to improve health opens major opportunities to develop and increase activity on general health promotion in the workplace. This has the advantage of covering all of the Key Areas. **The Government will set up a task force to examine and develop activity on health promotion in the workplace.** The Departments of Health and Employment, the Health and Safety Executive, the Health Education Authority, representatives from the Wider Health Working Group, the Confederation of British Industry, the Trades Union Congress and other business organisations will be invited to join. The objective will be to advise on new initiatives, including health promotion campaigns and on materials which can be produced for the workplace.

HEALTHY HOMES

3.25 The home environment affects many aspects of lifestyle and can have other important effects on health, for example, accidents. For some groups, such as children, parents, people not in outside employment and retired people, it is particularly important. Health professionals, particularly health visitors who work with families in their homes, and general practitioners have a major role in providing information and help so that people based at home can secure healthier ways of life for themselves and for members of their families.

3.26 Good housing is important to good health, although the interdependence between factors such as occupational class, income, unemployment, housing and lifestyle makes it difficult to assess which health effects are specifically attributable to it. The Government's objective is to ensure that decent housing is within the reach of all families. **The Government will continue to pursue its policies to promote choice and quality in housing, having regard to health and other benefits.**

HEALTHY PRISONS

3.27 In May 1992, the former Prison Medical Service was relaunched as the Health Care Service for Prisoners. This change of name signals a clear and increased commitment to health promotion, prevention of ill-health, and treatment. Major developments in health care for prisoners include:

- the establishment of a Health Advisory Committee, to advise on matters affecting the health of prisoners;

- the development of health standards in the prison setting;

- the development of an effective purchasing role through contracts with the NHS and other providers of clinical services.

HEALTHY ENVIRONMENTS

3.28 The quality of the environment is also an important influence on health. The Government White Paper "This Common Inheritance" set out the current targets for improving air and water quality and other environmental objectives which should, amongst other things, help to reduce risk factors to health. The next annual report on the environment later this year will update these targets, and will give particular attention to strengthening the links between environmental objectives and their health consequences. Areas for attention will include:

- *air quality standards* An Expert Panel on Air Quality Standards (EPAQS) has been set up to advise on standards and this panel will be supported by the Committee on the Medical Effects of Air Pollutants. Standards will be set or strengthened for concentrations of sulphur dioxide, ground level ozone, benzene, carbon monoxide, 1:3 butadiene and acid aerosols.

- *indoor air quality* Studies of the health effects of various indoor air pollutants including radon, volatile organic compounds, formaldehyde, nitrogen dioxide, mould spores and dust house mites are in hand. Advice on dealing with high levels of radon in homes is already available, with grants for remedial work in some cases. Guidance and other action on other contaminants will be developed as necessary.

- *drinking water* Ninety-nine per cent of the tests carried out on drinking water show compliance with regulatory standards. Quality is thoroughly audited by the Chief Drinking Water Inspector. Action to deal with remaining problems is in hand and will be extended, for example to deal with lead contamination in some areas.

- *exposure to UV radiation* International action is in hand to eliminate as soon as possible the production of CFCs and other substances which are damaging the ozone layer. A target for skin cancer is set in this White Paper (see *appendix, B.13*).

3.29 Often the most urgent priority is for research to pin-point more accurately the linkage between the quality of the environment and the health consequences. Having in mind the difficulty of establishing these linkages, the Government will explore the advantages of creating a new focus for work on environment and health in the form of a possible new Institute for the Environment and Health. Its work might cover risks to both human health and the natural environment from exposure to hazardous chemicals in the environment (already the National Radiological Protection Board has a similar responsibility for radiation hazards, and the Public Health Laboratory Service for microbiology). At present a variety of Government Departments and other public bodies share interests in this area, and improved co-ordination of work would ensure that effective programmes could be set up to address the most urgent problems.

THE SPECIAL ROLE OF HEALTH PROFESSIONALS

3.30 The role of the health professions – and indeed everyone who provides health care and related services – will be crucial to the success of the strategy. Their opportunities to help and advise individuals, families and communities are unparalleled.

3.31 The development and adoption of agreed standards of good practice is particularly important. The recent developments in clinical audit are to be commended and should be built on. Leadership in the development of good practice lies primarily with the health professions, and where appropriate, the voluntary sector.

3.32 The Government is keen to explore with professional, voluntary and other bodies opportunities for development and dissemination of standards of good practice, especially where this is developed collaboratively. **The Government's Chief Professional Officers will discuss with the health professions how further development of standards of good practice and clinical protocols can be taken forward.** The Government will also use new and existing machinery, such as the tripartite Task Group it has set up jointly with the General Medical Services Committee and the Royal College of General Practitioners to consider the identification and dissemination of good practice in health promotion for GPs.

3.33 The Department of Health will be exploring ways of creating national and local networks to draw together the scarce public health skills and widespread specialist knowledge needed to take the strategy for health forward.

PROFESSIONAL EDUCATION AND TRAINING

3.34 For any strategy to be successful it must be backed by appropriate initial and continuing education and training for all those whose work will be affected by the policies set out in this White Paper. For example, students in medical and dental undergraduate training need to appreciate that disease prevention and health promotion are as important as disease management and the provision of high quality care when considering the overall health of the population. **The Government will discuss the need for further emphasis on training in disease prevention and health promotion with the General Medical and Dental Councils who regulate the undergraduate curriculum and with the Royal Colleges and other bodies who have a key role in postgraduate and continuing medical education.**

3.35 In nurse education, Project 2000 is based on a health model which places emphasis on health promotion and disease prevention. The United Kingdom Central Council for Nursing, Midwifery and Health Visiting has consulted widely with the nursing professions on proposals for linking three-yearly re-registration with evidence of continuing education and training.

3.36 Similarly in pharmacy, changes in the degree course over recent years have reflected the changing role of the pharmacist and provide a new emphasis on health promotion and the provision of advice. The same issues will of course, apply to those many other professions involved in health services in the widest sense.

THE INTERNATIONAL DIMENSION

3.37 A successful health strategy cannot be insular. Threats to health may come just as easily from outside the United Kingdom as from within. Collaboration at international level encourages and facilitates the sharing of knowledge and research. Such collaboration in the past has led to the eradication of diseases such as smallpox: it is central to current work on HIV/AIDS. It ensures both a swifter identification of problems and solutions and the most economical use of scarce resources and skills.

3.38 The United Kingdom was a founder member of the World Health Organisation. Membership of the European Community and inter-Governmental co-operation on health matters adds a further and specific dimension. **The Government will build on these international links to bring the maximum benefit to the nation's health.**

4

THE ROLE OF THE NATIONAL HEALTH SERVICE

Central role of the NHS – Improving health – Action at all levels – National and local targets – Supporting local development – Health education by the NHS – NHS as a healthy employer

4.1 The goals, objectives and targets in this White Paper are for the nation as a whole. However, as the main provider of health care, the National Health Service is uniquely placed to promote health and set an example to other organisations in the country. Improving health should be the prime concern of every NHS authority and health professional and manager in the NHS.

4.2 The Government's reforms of the NHS mean that health authorities can now respond strategically to the health needs of the populations they serve. They have begun to ensure that services are fully co-ordinated. Above all, they have improved systems of accountability and introduced the concept of targets so that each part of the NHS can be actively managed, monitored and improved.

THE CHALLENGE FOR THE NHS

4.3 The *continuing success* of the NHS is in improving quality of care, reducing waiting times, and increasing efficiency and value for money. The *challenge* for the NHS is to establish a more direct link between what it does and the results in terms of improved health both for individuals and the population more widely. To help achieve this, the NHS can mobilise local action through healthy alliances and explore with other organisations and groups the common ground on health issues. It can provide expertise, assistance with negotiations and monitoring of agreements in respect of joint operational health programmes and strategic target setting.

ACTION BY NHS – SECURING THE CHANGE

4.4 At **national level** the Key Areas and targets for quality and service will be at the core of the overall objectives for the NHS. **Increasingly, NHS authorities' performance will be measured against the efficient use of resources, and working with others, to achieve improvements in the** *health* **of local people.**

4.5 At **regional level** Regional Health Authorities (RHAs) will lead in ensuring that objectives are achieved. They are already setting regional health goals in addition to national objectives.

4.6 The NHS Management Executive will require RHAs to consolidate this ground-work into more developed regional strategies within the Key Areas of the national strategy and those identified locally. Specifically, the NHS Management Executive will look to RHAs to:

- develop and agree local health and service targets for District Health Authorities (DHAs) and Family Health Services Authorities (FHSAs);

- ensure DHAs and FHSAs develop purchasing and health investment plans to deliver health objectives, including joint plans where appropriate;

- encourage DHAs and FHSAs to shift the focus towards health promotion (including changing the balance of resources as necessary);

- act as a focal point for health in their area and develop healthy alliances with other agencies at regional level;

- support the professions in the development and promotion of good practice;

- promote appropriate research and development.

4.7 At **local level** DHAs and FHSAs will form healthy alliances and will jointly agree local targets. Purchasing and health investment plans will be developed which deliver agreed health objectives. DHAs and FHSAs will integrate services where appropriate to meet specific health needs. In addition, joint purchasing arrangements will be agreed with other authorities within and outside the NHS. Community Health Councils (CHCs) will have the opportunity to comment during the target setting process, and to monitor performance against agreed targets. DHAs and FHSAs should work closely with regional and local media to get across health messages and to ensure local consultation on health questions.

4.8 Hospital and Community Units will need to reassess the services they provide and confirm with DHAs, FHSAs, GPs, CHCs and local people that they are meeting local needs and improving health.

4.9 Primary and community health care services will have a major role. Success in Key Areas will depend greatly on the commitment and skills of family and community doctors, nurses, midwives and health visitors, dentists, community pharmacists, opticians and other professionals working in the community. **The Department of Health and the NHS Management Executive will work with the professions nationally, and managers and clinicians at local level, to explore ways of developing existing health promotion arrangements in primary care in response to the national strategy.**

NATIONAL TARGETS AND LOCAL TARGETS

4.10 National targets will be translated into regional and local action in the NHS. Improvements in health will take time to achieve and, particularly at regional and local level, will take time to show up as statistically significant. Improvements will need to be tracked over time. In some instances, therefore, annual monitoring will have to make use of other indicators of health improvement (such as reductions in risk factors), improvements in services (for example, immunisation), and other outputs which can be measured annually. **The Department of Health and the NHS Management Executive will commission further work on the development of methods for setting and monitoring such health targets at local level.**

SUPPORTING LOCAL DEVELOPMENT

4.11 The Department of Health and NHS Management Executive will continue to support local development of the skills and strategies needed to meet objectives and targets. In particular the Management Executive will:

● set up NHS 'focus groups' in each of the Key Areas to give a lead to NHS authorities nationally;

● commission handbooks on possible local approaches to Key Areas within the national strategy, to be ready later in 1992 in time to contribute to the planning process for 1993-94;

and

● establish a network of regional "Health of the Nation" co-ordinators, and further encourage the development of good communication between RHAs to ensure that all NHS authorities have access to, and draw on, the experience and achievements of others.

HEALTH EDUCATION BY THE NHS

4.12 The NHS will improve health education at local level, so that people are able to make informed decisions about their own health and that of their families. The Department of Health and the NHS Management Executive are reviewing with NHS Authorities and the Health Education Authority the role of health authorities in health education, and in particular the way in which authorities are supported by the HEA. The results of this review will be available by the autumn, and **a campaign of action to improve health education activity by the NHS will be developed for implementation from 1993.**

THE NHS AS A HEALTHY EMPLOYER

4.13 The NHS must set an example to other employers and show what can be achieved. The NHS Management Executive has set up a task group of NHS managers, HEA respresentatives and professionals to review the way in which the NHS promotes the health of its own employees. **The group will bring**

forward proposals for national and local targets, including proposals for units, health centres, GP practices and other workplaces in the NHS to declare themselves 'healthy workplaces'.

CONCLUSION: BUILDING ON SUCCESS

4.14 The NHS is already responding positively to "The Health of the Nation". Its contribution to the strategy will be significant and will mark a profound change in the NHS – as measurable improvements in *health* becomes as important to the service as the delivery of *health care*.

5

MONITORING, DEVELOPING AND REVIEWING THE STRATEGY

Monitoring health – The Central Health Monitoring Unit – New national health surveys – Health outcomes assessment – Information strategy – NHS information – Research – Periodic reports on progress

5.1 "The Health of the Nation" Green Paper emphasised that the strategy and its targets must be underpinned by adequate systems for:

● monitoring and appraising the health of the population

● research

● measurement of health outcomes.

5.2 This chapter sets out the further progress which has been made and the action which is being taken specifically to support the health strategy. It also addresses how the strategy will be reviewed and developed.

MONITORING HEALTH – DEVELOPING THE INFORMATION BASE FOR THE HEALTH OF THE NATION

5.3 Information needed to develop the health strategy and monitor progress is extensive in some areas and less good in others. Overall, more comprehensive health monitoring information is needed both nationally and locally. Relevant initiatives include:

(a) New national health surveys

"The Health of the Nation" Green Paper announced the development of a new health survey programme for England. This contains two elements: an annual general health and nutrition survey and biennial detailed dietary and nutrition surveys. **The health and nutrition survey is being expanded from 1992/93**

to cover, in due course, a sample in excess of 15,000 adults. The scope for using this new survey to fill information gaps in other, or potential, Key Areas is being considered. A proposed **Mental Health Morbidity Survey** should provide much needed information on the prevalence of mental illness in the community.

The development of the new national health surveys needs to be mirrored at Regional, District and Family Health Services Authority levels. The Department of Health, in conjunction with the NHS, proposes to establish an NHS survey advisory centre to examine data available from existing surveys, to ascertain NHS authorities' needs for such material, to assess the suitability of survey methodologies, to promote research into methodologies and to promulgate advice to NHS authorities.

(b) Central Health Monitoring Unit: epidemiological overviews

The Central Health Monitoring Unit was set up to improve the Department of Health's analyses of the epidemiological data which underpins the formulation and implementation of policy. It is publishing a **new series of epidemiological overviews.** The first overview, on elderly people, will be followed by others covering such topics as asthma, coronary heart disease and stroke.

The Department is also considering how it can **further improve the ways in which it can disseminate more widely information about the state of the public health.**

(c) Health outcomes assessment

The Department of Health has established a Central Health Outcomes Unit to lead in developing health outcomes assessment – the assessment of the health benefits of particular health care or other interventions. The Unit will co-ordinate the development of the Outcomes Clearing House and the work on the development of outcome indicators announced in "The Health of the Nation" Green Paper.

(d) Information strategy

The Department of Health is developing information strategies to ensure that it collects the information required to support its objectives in the most cost-effective way. One of the strategies – the Public Health Information Strategy – is currently examining how best to improve morbidity and disability information. **Development of this information strategy will be guided by the priorities set out in this White Paper.**

(e) Annual Health Reports of Directors of Public Health

Directors of Public Health are responsible for monitoring the health and the health care needs of their population. They are required to produce annual health reports to provide information about the health of their population, to report progress and to identify areas for further improvement. Annual health reports are the prime vehicle for presenting information about health at a local level and have the potential to provide key information necessary for monitoring and developing the national strategy. **In order to realise their potential the Department of Health will initiate discussions with Directors of Public Health and their professional organisations to explore how the role of annual health reports can be enhanced in monitoring, reviewing and developing the strategy for health.**

(f) NHS information

The NHS reforms have placed great emphasis on the flow of information from providers to purchasers in support of contracts. With information systems focused on the health record of the individual patient, details of all interventions, treatments and outcomes over time and across all service providers and agencies can be obtained, provided arrangements to safeguard confidentiality are strictly observed. This will particularly help DHAs as purchasers to build up information about patterns of care and about what is happening to their residents in terms of health events. DHAs and FHSAs will also be able to draw together other information affecting health to help in their assessments of needs.

(g) Environment and health

The Department of the Environment will be developing and maintaining a series of data on the main forms of pollution of the atmosphere, water and land. As the linkages between such pollutants and possible health effects become progressively better understood, it will be important also to establish machinery for monitoring such health impacts. The Department of Health and the Department of the Environment will work together on this and there may be an important role here for the new Institute suggested in *chapter 3*.

RESEARCH

5.4 Research is essential to any strategy to improve health. A broad Department of Health Research and Development (R&D) strategy covers the Department's and NHS's own research programme and interaction with R&D in other Government Departments, Medical and other Research Councils, charities, industry and the European Community. **Increasingly, research will be oriented towards attaining objectives within Key Areas and towards contributing new knowledge in other areas which will allow the health strategy to develop and broaden over time.**

5.5 Through the Medical Research Council (MRC), the Government funds extensive research which has as its ultimate objective the maintenance and improvement of human health. MRC funding has risen by about 28% in real terms since 1979 and it has contributed substantially to the research on which the targets in this White Paper are based. The Health Departments have recently renegotiated the Concordat governing the relationship between them and the MRC to help ensure that emphasis is placed on NHS and Health Departments' needs, including "Health of the Nation" priorities, as well as scientific opportunities.

5.6 A new R&D strategy for the NHS was launched in April 1991. The prime objective of the strategy is to ensure that care in the NHS is based on high quality research relevant to improving the nation's health. In setting priorities for NHS R&D, opportunities for work which help the NHS increase its efficiency and promote health will have priority. **NHS R&D priorities will reflect the strategy established by this White Paper.** The Central Research and Development Committee – and the regional R&D committees – will look both at what research the NHS can contribute to achieving targets in Key Areas, and also at the work which could be put in hand to allow targets to be set and achieved in other areas where this is not yet possible.

REVIEWING AND DEVELOPING THE STRATEGY

5.7 To be successful, the strategy for health must be dynamic, with regular reviews, assessment and reassessment of priorities.

5.8 Systematic review of progress towards achievement of targets in Key Areas is central to "The Health of the Nation" initiative. Some health outcomes will take time to emerge clearly. It will therefore also be important to monitor progress on the development of the structures and processes which will help generate the improvements in health.

5.9 The strategy also needs to continue to develop: some initial Key Areas may, over time, cease to continue to warrant priority status, or it may become appropriate to add new Key Areas. The Government therefore intends:

- *first,* that the **Department of Health will publish a detailed appraisal of information and indicators needed to monitor progress in each Key Area** – this will consider what is needed, in what form and how it might be used;

- *second,* that **periodic reports on the progress of "The Health of the Nation" initiative as a whole be published, with reviews of the strategy on a regular basis.**

5.10 The Ministerial Committee on Health Strategy, supported by the three "Health of the Nation" Working Groups *(chapter 3),* **will oversee the development and progress of the initiative as a whole.**

CONCLUSION

5.11 "The Health of the Nation" initiative represents a major step forward in improving the health of the people of England. At its heart is the setting, for the first time in England, of an initial set of priority *health* targets at which the nation as a whole can aim, together with new action to focus effort on the target areas. This White Paper starts the process: the sole measure of its success will be what it contributes to the achievement of these targets and others which are developed over time.

APPENDIX

This appendix describes in greater detail the nature of each Key Area and the approach to be taken to meet targets (Sections A-E). It also discusses the relevance of Key Areas to specific population groups (Section F).

SECTION A	**Coronary heart disease and stroke**
SECTION B	**Cancers**
SECTION C	**Mental illness**
SECTION D	**HIV/AIDS and sexual health**
SECTION E	**Accidents**
SECTION F	**Key Areas and the health of people in specific groups of the population**

SECTION A

CORONARY HEART DISEASE AND STROKE

INTRODUCTION

A.1 Coronary Heart Disease (CHD) accounted for about 26% of deaths in England in 1991. It is both the single largest cause of death, and the single main cause of premature death. It accounts for 2.5% of total NHS expenditure, and results in 35 million lost working days per year.

A.2 Approximately 12% of all deaths in 1991 resulted from stroke, which is also a major cause of disability, particularly amongst elderly people. Stroke accounts for 6% of total NHS expenditure and results in the loss of about 7.7 million working days each year.

A.3 Although the death rate for CHD in England has been declining since the late 1970s, it remains one of the highest in the world. Mortality from stroke in England has also declined and fell by about 40% in both men and women between 1971 and 1991.

A.4 It is generally accepted that the main risk factors for CHD and stroke are:

- cigarette smoking
- raised plasma cholesterol
- raised blood pressure
- lack of physical activity.

Plasma cholesterol is particularly important in setting the baseline level of CHD risk. Raised blood pressure is the most important risk factor for stroke. Other predictors of risk, such as socioeconomic factors, influences in early life and stress, are less well understood.

A.5 All the main risk factors can be influenced by changes in behaviour. For those who smoke, stopping smoking is the single most effective means of reducing risk for CHD and stroke. Excessive dietary intake of saturated fatty acids results in raised plasma cholesterol levels. Excessive consumption of alcohol, and of sodium (mainly as sodium chloride – common salt) contribute to raised blood pressure. Obesity contributes to both raised plasma cholesterol levels and raised blood pressure. Obesity results from a dietary energy intake chronically in excess of energy expenditure and is thus related to both diet and physical activity. Physical activity also acts directly to reduce the risk of CHD and stroke. Beneficial effects on CHD or stroke should therefore result from:

- stopping smoking
- reducing consumption of saturated fatty acids and sodium
- reducing alcohol consumption
- increasing physical activity.

A.6 Because these factors can be influenced, much heart disease and stroke is potentially preventable. People of all ages can reduce their risk of CHD and stroke. Even late in life, changes in lifestyle can give considerable benefits.

OBJECTIVE

To reduce the level of ill-health and death caused by coronary heart disease and stroke, and the risk factors associated with them.

MAIN TARGETS

A. **To reduce death rates for both CHD and stroke in people under 65 by at least 40% by the year 2000 (from 58 per 100,000 population in 1990 to no more than 35 per 100,000 for CHD, and from 12.5 per 100,000 population in 1990 to no more than 7.5 per 100,000 for stroke).**

B. **To reduce the death rate for CHD in people aged 65 to 74 by at least 30% by the year 2000 (from 899 per 100,000 population in 1990 to no more than 629 per 100,000).**

C. **To reduce the death rate for stroke in people aged 65 to 74 by at least 40% by the year 2000 (from 265 per 100,000 population in 1990 to no more than 159 per 100,000).**

Notes on targets A-C

The main emphasis of this Section is on the primary prevention of CHD and stroke. However, reductions in mortality are also expected to result from improvements in the effectiveness of treatment and rehabilitation services.

A.7 *Figures 6* and *7* show trends in death rates from CHD and stroke, and the target. If CHD and stroke are to be tackled successfully, action and innovation will be needed throughout the country by a wide range of organisations and individuals. Some strategies will need to consider the totality of the problem, others will concentrate on individual aspects of it.

(a)   General action

A.8 Every individual should be helped to be aware of the risk factors associated with CHD and stroke and how to make the lifestyle changes necessary to avoid them. They also need to be encouraged and supported in making – and sustaining – decisions based on this information.

A.9 National leadership will be required from the Government, national bodies such as the National Forum for Coronary Heart Disease Prevention and its constituent organisations, and professional leaders in medicine, nursing, nutrition and other disciplines. Others with opportunities to contribute include local government, the education sector, producers of food, industry, employers and employees in the workplace, and the media.

"Look After Your Heart"

A.10 The joint Department of Health/Health Education Authority "Look After Your Heart" programme has a five year strategy, "Beating Heart Disease in the 1990s". It aims to provide information to the public and to help make the most of opportunities that exist everywhere to tackle CHD.

National Health Service

A.11 The NHS has a significant contribution to make to all aspects of CHD and stroke prevention, as a provider of services for prevention, early detection, treatment and rehabilitation, and also as an advocate for health and as an employer.

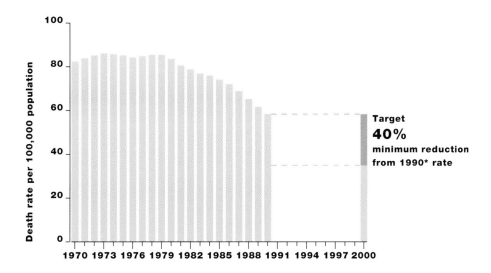

Death rates for Coronary Heart Disease

England 1970-1990** and target for the year 2000
All persons aged under 65°

Source: OPCS (ICD 410:414)

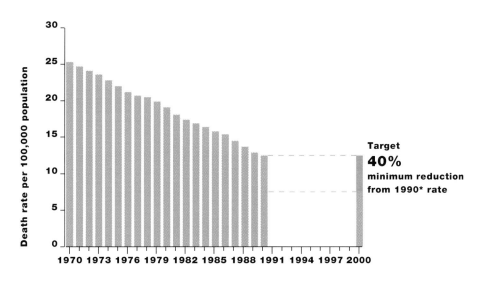

Death rates for Stroke

England 1970-1990** and target for the year 2000
All persons aged under 65°

Source: OPCS (ICD 430:438)

* Rates are calculated using a 3 year average plotted against the middle year of average
• The change in classification between the years 1978 and 1979, and a change in coding
  procedures between 1983 and 1984 may affect the comparability of the data
° Rates are calculated using the European Standard Population to take into account
  differences in age structure

Death rates for Coronary Heart Disease

England 1970-1990*• and target for the year 2000
All persons aged 65-74

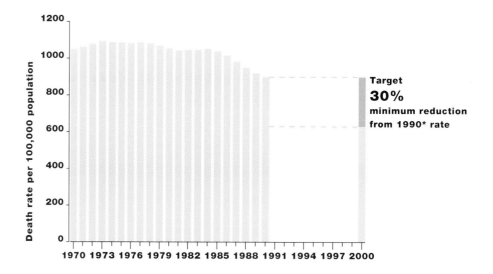

Source: OPCS (ICD 410:414)

Death rates for Stroke

England 1970-1990*• and target for the year 2000
All persons aged 65-74

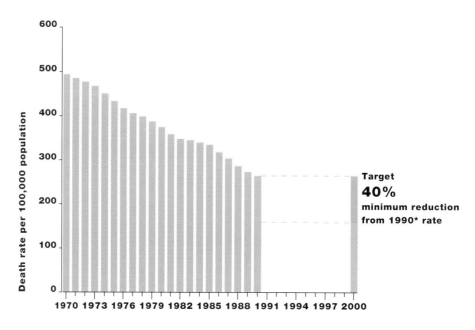

Source: OPCS (ICD 430:438)

* Rates are calculated using a 3 year average plotted against the middle year of average

• The change in classification between the years 1978 and 1979, and a change in coding procedures between 1983 and 1984 may affect the comparability of the data

A.12 The Government believes that in the long term it is in the area of prevention that there is the greatest potential for overall improvement in health. However, it wishes to ensure that improvements in treatment and rehabilitation services continue and that standards of good practice are set and adhered to. Professional leadership is required. One area that might be explored locally is the measurement and reduction of the time between onset of symptoms and institution of thrombolytic therapy in patients with acute myocardial infarction.

Research

A.13 Continued research is necessary into the most appropriate and cost-effective ways of preventing and treating CHD and stroke. The Government is committed to establishing close working relationships with major research funding bodies in this field. To this end, a research liaison committee has been established.

(b)   Smoking

> **D.   To reduce the prevalence of cigarette smoking in men and women aged 16 and over to no more than 20% by the year 2000 (a reduction of at least 35% in men and 29% in women, from a prevalence in 1990 of 31% and 28% respectively).**

Note on target D
> See Section B for full smoking targets.

A.14 Smoking is estimated to account for up to 18% of CHD deaths and up to 11% of stroke deaths. Strategies for reducing smoking are described in Section B.

(c) Diet and Nutrition

E. To reduce the average percentage of food energy derived by the population from saturated fatty acids by at least 35% by 2005 (from 17% in 1990 to no more than 11%).

F. To reduce the average percentage of food energy derived by the population from total fat by at least 12% by 2005 (from about 40% in 1990 to no more than 35%).

Notes on targets E-F

Regular data are already collected through the National Food Survey on average population intakes of fat and fatty acids.

A.15 Eating a variety of foods which gives a good balance of nutrients is vital for the repair and maintenance of every part of the body throughout life. Current evidence suggests that dietary factors are mainly responsible, through plasma cholesterol, for setting the baseline level of CHD risk in the population, and act together with other risk factors. The eating habits of the population also play a significant part in the development and prevention of stroke, as blood pressure is affected by both obesity and sodium intake.

A.16 Dietary changes which would help prevent CHD and stroke have been identified by the Committee on the Medical Aspects of Food Policy (COMA), most recently in the 1991 report on Dietary Reference Values. The targets set represent the major elements of this advice. COMA is currently reviewing its advice on diet and cardiovascular disease and a further report is expected in early 1993.

A.17 Action to achieve health and nutrition targets involves the dissemination of information about healthy eating and encouraging and enabling changes in the population's diet. A whole diet approach is crucial if the balance of the diet is to be sensible. To reach the targets in a diet that also matches COMA's wider recommendations, patterns of food consumption will need to change very considerably.

In pursuit of this the Government will, in collaboration with others as appropriate:

- **continue and enhance research into the links between diet and health, and into influences on consumer choice;**
- **continue to secure expert advice on nutrition and health;**
- **continue national surveillance of diet, nutrition and health of the population;**
- **seek ways of improving and targeting information and advice on healthy eating and weight control;**
- **seek ways of improving information on the nutritional content of food;**
- **produce and disseminate voluntary nutritional guidelines for catering outlets.**

A.18 Co-ordinated action is needed from a range of interested parties. **The Government proposes to set up a joint Nutrition Task Force, which would be a partnership of officials from relevant Government Departments and representatives from other sectors identified in** *figure 8*. The Task Force will seek to harness and facilitate the contributions of all those involved. *Figure 8* gives examples of the range of opportunities open to each agent.

OPPORTUNITIES FOR PROMOTING HEALTHY EATING

Figure

Health Education Authority
- continuing to develop nutrition education resources for health professionals and for the public

Food producers, manufacturers and retailers
- increasing further the variety and availability of manufactured foods with lower saturates, fat and sodium content than in current versions
- reformulating more standard foods as far as practicable to reduce saturates, fat and sodium
- offering throughout the country plentiful and easily accessible supplies of starchy staples, vegetables and fruit
- moving at an early date to full nutrition labelling
- developing marketing practices more conducive to healthy food choices

Caterers
- offering menus which enable and encourage people to choose healthy diets
- using Government nutritional guidelines
- identifying models of healthy catering practice and disseminating them throughout the catering network
- ensuring adequate nutrition education and training of professional and other catering staff

Health and local authority services
- ensuring adequate nutrition education and training of all appropriate professional and other staff
- ensuring adequate dietetic expertise in the health and education sectors
- maximising opportunities for educating people about healthy eating
- encouraging the use of Government nutritional guidelines in catering facilities

Media/ advertisers
- giving the public information about diet, nutrition and health which encourages healthy eating

Voluntary sector
- taking initiatives nationally and locally which support the aim of encouraging healthy eating
- co-ordinating activities within the voluntary sector and with Government and others

(d)   Obesity

G.   To reduce the percentages of men and women aged 16-64 who are obese by at least 25% for men and at least 33% for women by 2005 (from 8% for men and 12% for women in 1986/87 to no more than 6% and 8% respectively).

Note on target G

> Obesity = Body Mass Index of 30+ (weight in kgs divided by height in m²). The target will be monitored through the national health survey programme as well as the new national diet and nutrition survey programme, which covers a different age group every two years; both of these will in the future include elderly people.

A.19 Obesity acts to increase the risk of CHD and stroke through its association with an increased prevalence of raised blood pressure and raised plasma cholesterol. Obesity results from dietary energy intake chronically in excess of energy expenditure, and so is related to both diet and physical activity. Overweight and obesity (Body Mass Index greater than 25 and 30 respectively) are increasing in both men and women. In 1986/87 24% of women and 37% of men were overweight. In addition a further 12% of women and 8% of men were obese, compared to 8% and 6% respectively in 1980. If the target were achieved, the prevalence of obesity would be reduced to its level at the start of the 1980s, thus reversing the trend of recent years. Action set out under 'diet and nutrition' and 'physical activity' will be important in helping to achieve the obesity target.

(e)   Plasma Cholesterol

A.20 The risk of CHD increases with rising plasma cholesterol levels. It has been estimated that a reduction in the average plasma cholesterol level of the population of 10% might in time result in a 20-30% reduction in CHD mortality.

A.21 In 1986/87 about two-thirds of the British adult population under 65 had plasma cholesterol levels above the desirable range (less than 5.2 mmol/l). Levels of plasma cholesterol were higher in those eating a high proportion of saturated fatty acids and in those who were obese or overweight. It has been estimated that achievement of the dietary target to reduce intake of saturated fatty acids from its present average level of 17% to an average of 11% of food energy will lead to a reduction in plasma cholesterol of 0.4–0.5 mmol/l in the population. Plasma cholesterol levels in the population will be monitored nationally through the new national health survey programme (see *chapter 5*). In this way, the outcome resulting from achievement of the dietary targets will be monitored, as well as achievement of the targets themselves.

A.22 Following the Standing Medical Advisory Committee's Report on the Cost–effectiveness of Cholesterol Testing, **the Government will issue guidance on how the Committee's conclusions might be reflected in local strategies to combat CHD.**

(f)   Blood Pressure

> **H. To reduce mean systolic blood pressure in the adult population by at least 5mm Hg by 2005.**

Note on target H
> This will be monitored nationally through the new national health survey programme (see Chapter 5). This programme will also determine the baseline level of systolic blood pressure in the adult population.

A.23 Raised blood pressure is associated with obesity and overweight, excessive alcohol consumption, high sodium (principally from salt) and low potassium intakes. The relationship between blood pressure and CHD is continuous and of the same order as the relationship between blood cholesterol and CHD. The relationship between blood pressure and stroke is stronger. Significant public health gains would be expected from reducing the average blood pressure level of the whole population and from the detection and appropriate treatment of raised blood pressure in individuals. A reduction in mean blood pressure in the population of 5mm Hg could be expected from success in achieving the obesity and alcohol targets, together with a reduction in sodium intake. It has been estimated that such a reduction would result in a 10% reduction in mortality from CHD and stroke.

(g)   Alcohol

I.   **To reduce the proportion of men drinking more than 21 units of alcohol per week from 28% in 1990 to 18% by 2005, and the proportion of women drinking more than 14 units of alcohol per week from 11% in 1990 to 7% by 2005.**

Note on target I

> The UK medical profession advises that sustained alcohol consumption in excess of 21 units per week for men and 14 units per week for women is likely to lead to increasing health risks (see *figure 9*). The baseline percentages in the target statement are taken from 1990 General Household Survey, and progress towards achieving the targets will be monitored nationally. Currently this information is available from questions included biennially in the General Household Survey. The Government will also monitor nationally a number of other indicators of alcohol misuse, eg numbers drinking in excess of the dangerous levels (50 units per week for men and 35 units for women), liver cirrhosis deaths, and deaths in alcohol-related road traffic accidents.

Figure 9

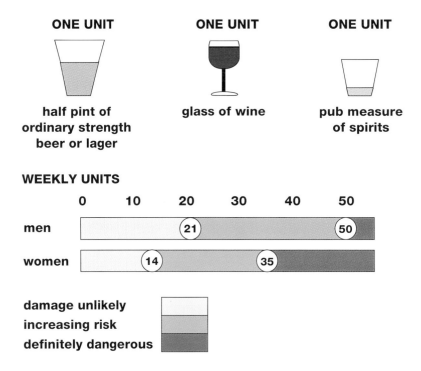

Alcohol Consumption Guidelines

A.24 The consumption of alcohol in sensible quantities and in appropriate circumstances provides many people with enjoyment[1]. But there is a difference between sensible drinking, and excessive or inappropriate drinking. Drinking less than 21 units per week by men or 14 units per week by women is unlikely to damage health (see *figure 9*). Sustained drinking in excess of these levels progressively increases the risk of raised blood pressure and stroke, and possibly CHD. In addition it is associated with other conditions, including various cancers and liver cirrhosis. The treatment of alcohol-related disorders leads to significant demands on health authority expenditure. Alcohol consumption on inappropriate occasions can lead to accidents, and in particular, drinking should be avoided before driving. It is estimated that eight million working days are lost annually through alcohol-related absenteeism.

---

[1] There have been some studies which suggest that moderate drinking may reduce some of the risk factors associated with CHD, but there is as yet no scientific consensus on the overall impact on the incidence of CHD of alcohol consumption within recommended sensible limits.

A.25 In 1987, the Government launched an inter-departmental campaign to promote sensible drinking and reduce alcohol misuse. Initiatives included measures to reduce alcohol-related crime and the incidence of under-age drinking, the renegotiation of the alcohol advertising code of practice, and action to deter drink/driving. Progress is summarised in the report "Action Against Alcohol Misuse" published in December 1991. These initiatives will continue, and additional action by Government to help achieve the targets will include the following:

- **health will be one of the factors which the Chancellor of the Exchequer will take into account in deciding the appropriate level of alcohol duties in any year**

- **the commitment within the framework of the family health services to the promotion of the sensible drinking message will be strengthened**

- **an agreed format for the display of customer information on alcohol units at point of sale will be considered jointly with the alcohol trade associations**

- **there will be a new initiative to monitor the penetration of the sensible drinking message**

- **employers will continue to be encouraged to introduce workplace alcohol policies, and to evaluate their impact**

- **the expansion and improvement of voluntary sector service provision will be supported, including the provision of additional funds through an allocation to Alcohol Concern (£4 million over three years), and through alcohol and drugs specific grants (£2.1 million in 1992/93).**

A.26 As with diet and nutrition, concerted action will be required if the problems connected with excessive and inappropriate consumption of alcohol are to be tackled successfully. *Figure 10* illustrates the range of those involved, and the challenges and opportunities open to them.

OPPORTUNITIES FOR REDUCING EXCESSIVE AND
INAPPROPRIATE CONSUMPTION OF ALCOHOL   *Figure 10*

Health education

- The Health Education Authority will continue to publish health educational material, to develop local health education networks and to manage the Drinkwise campaign.

- In schools, the National Curriculum now requires children between 7 and 16 to be taught about the effects of alcohol on the way the human body functions.

**National
Health
Service**

- Further promotion of sensible drinking messages will be needed at all levels in the NHS. District Health Authorities (DHAs) will also need to work with local authorities to ensure that a full range of services is provided for helping problem drinkers and their families. DHAs should seek to ensure that they are party to an agreed inter-agency alcohol misuse strategy.

- Policy formation in greatly helped by access to quantified information on people's drinking habits. Special surveys can be undertaken as part of the development of the public health function, and all DHAs should consider whether this would form an appropriate part of their needs assessment. Professional bodies are encouraging the formation of general practice profiles by aggregating quantified drinking histories derived from routine screening.

- DHAs should explore with medical staff the extent to which routine hospital admission procedures should include taking quantified information about each patient's drinking history, so that action can be taken and advice offered as necessary. This will be discussed with professional bodies at national level.

OPPORTUNITIES FOR REDUCING EXCESSIVE AND
INAPPROPRIATE CONSUMPTION OF ALCOHOL (Continued)

- Primary health care professionals will be encouraged within the context of schemes developed by DHAs and Family Health Service Authorities, to identify the scope for health promotion initiatives. Family doctors are already expected as part of their terms of service to take account of their patients' alcohol consumption, and many already collect quantified information.

Local authorities
- Social Services Departments will continue to develop services for helping problem drinkers and their families within the framework of community care.

- Local authority road safety officers will continue to mount local campaigns to deter drink/driving.

Voluntary sector
- Voluntary organisations provide services for helping problem drinkers and their families, and will need to plan for developments within the framework of community care. They also continue to contribute to the promulgation of the sensible drinking message.

Caring professions
- Professional bodies in health and social work will continue to design training to promote the early identification of alcohol misuse, and appropriate referral skills.

- The Government is pursuing an initiative to heighten the awareness of nurses, midwives and health visitors of the incidence of alcohol misuse.

Alcohol producers
- The Portman Group, the alcohol industry's initiative against alcohol misuse, will continue to promote sensible drinking in collaboration with the HEA.

Employers
- Employers can contribute by developing and implementing workplace alcohol policies, including the referral of staff with alcohol problems for specialist help.

(h)   Physical Activity

A.27 Physical activity not only contributes to the prevention and management of overweight and obesity but also affords direct protection against CHD.

A.28 The results of a national study of physical activity – the Allied Dunbar National Fitness Survey, sponsored by Allied Dunbar, the HEA, Sports Council and Department of Health – were published in June this year. Results indicate that, overall, the population of England is not very physically active, and that levels of cardio-respiratory (aerobic) fitness in the population are extremely low – about one third of middle-aged men and one half of middle-aged women are "unfit" for continuous walking on the level at a normal pace (about 3 mph).

A.29 The Government will, in consultation with others, develop detailed strategies for physical activity in the light of the survey results.

A.30 Strategies to achieve targets for physical activity will involve national and local government, individuals, voluntary and community organisations, HEA, the Sports Council, Regional Sports Councils and other sports bodies, schools, employers, the media, the leisure industry, the NHS and others.

A.31 One important step already taken is the decision to include physical education in the National Curriculum. This means that it will be a compulsory subject for all pupils aged 5 to 16 in maintained schools. The statutory Order for National Curriculum physical education was laid before Parliament in March 1992 and will begin to come into effect in schools in August 1992. The provisions stress the importance of physical activity and require pupils to show that they recognise its importance and the effect that activity – or the lack of it – can have on the body.

A.32 In December 1991 the Government set out in its policy statement on "Sport and Active Recreation" proposals for improving the opportunities available to young people to take part in sport and active recreation. Guidance will be published later this year on good practice in promoting partnerships between schools and other organisations in the local community. The policy statement also announced the new Sports Council for England which will have, as one of its main functions, the promotion of participation in sport and active recreation by the population in general.

A.33 In September 1991 the Government issued a new planning guidance note on sport and recreation which emphasised the importance it placed on the provision of land and water resources for organised sport and informal recreation. It advised planning authorities to take account of the local community's need for recreational facilities when making day to day development control decisions and when forming development plans. It also advised planning authorities to resist pressures for the development of open space which would conflict with the wider public interest.

VARIATIONS

A.34 There are considerable variations in rates of CHD and stroke deaths between different areas of the country, different black and ethnic minority groups and different occupational groups. Generally, rates are higher in the north of the country, and amongst manual workers. (The pattern in the latter case is more marked for stroke.) Differences amongst occupational groups may, in part, be accounted for by differences in smoking prevalence. The influence of alcohol intake on variations is less clear-cut. Whilst manual groups include a higher proportion of heavy drinkers than non-manual groups, they also have a higher proportion of people who never drink, or who drink only very lightly and infrequently. Amongst minority ethnic groups, mortality rates for CHD are higher than the white population in people (especially women) who have originated from the Indian sub-continent, but lower in those of Afro-Caribbean origin. On the other hand, this latter group has higher rates of stroke.

CONSEQUENTIAL IMPROVEMENTS IN HEALTH

A.35 Consequential improvements in health which would be delivered by success in tackling coronary heart disease, stroke and their associated risk factors will include:

(a) Related to diet and nutrition

There is increasing evidence that, as well as reducing the risk of CHD and stroke, a diet relatively low in fat and rich in vegetables and fruit is associated with lower risk of a variety of cancers, including those of the breast and bowel. Obesity carries increased risk of a number of other conditions in addition to CHD and stroke, and is associated with osteoarthritis, gallstones, non-insulin dependent diabetes and increased fatality from post-menopausal breast cancer. Diabetes is itself known to be a risk factor for both CHD and stroke. It has been estimated that people with diabetes mellitus have a two- to four-fold greater risk of death from CHD and stroke.

(b) Related to alcohol misuse

Reducing the number of people drinking excessively would play a part in reducing cancers of the mouth cavity, pharynx, larynx and oesophagus (particularly if combined with a reduction in smoking), liver cirrhosis, pancreatitis and endocrine disorders. Excessive consumption is also associated with a variety of social problems.

(c) Related to physical activity

Physical activity also contributes to bone strength (thereby reducing the prevalence of osteoporosis), muscle strength and power and joint flexibility.

SECTION B

CANCERS

INTRODUCTION

B.1 After coronary heart disease, cancers are the most common cause of death in England, accounting for about 25% of deaths in 1991. There are many types of cancers. Understanding of the causes of these varies greatly, as does current ability to prevent, treat and cure them.

B.2 Though the factors affecting cancer incidence are by no means fully understood, it is clear that genetic, behavioural and environmental factors all have a role.

Smoking has been shown to contribute to approximately 30% of all cancer deaths and is responsible for at least 80% of those from lung cancer.

There is mounting, though as yet inconclusive, evidence that *diets* relatively low in meat and fat, and high in vegetables, starchy staple foods, cereals and fruits may be associated with a lower occurrence of cancers of the stomach and large bowel, breast, ovary and prostate. Obesity is also associated with an increased occurrence of cancers of the gall bladder and uterus, and increased fatality from breast cancer in later life.

Environmental factors make a small but important contribution to the overall cancer mortality. It has been estimated that geophysical factors – ultra-violet light and background ionising radiation — may account for about 3% of all cancer deaths. Of lung cancer deaths it is estimated that around 5% (some 1,600 per year in England) might be partially attributed to exposure to *radon*. However, there is an interaction between radon and smoking, and it has been estimated that the risk to smokers from radon is about ten times that for non-smokers.

B.3 There are a number of simple things which individuals can do to contribute to the prevention and early detection of many cancers. These are set out in the

European Code Against Cancer, or "Ten Commandments" – see *figure 11*. The Government and the European Commission have supported widespread dissemination of the Code to the public and to health professionals.

Figure 11

European Code Against Cancer, or "Ten Commandments"

1. Do not smoke. Smokers, stop as quickly as possible and do not smoke in the presence of others.

2. Moderate your consumption of alcoholic drinks – beers, wines and spirits.

3. Avoid excessive exposure to the sun.

4. Follow health and safety instructions at work concerning production, handling or use of any substance which may cause cancer.

5. Frequently eat fresh fruit and vegetables, and cereals with a high fibre content.

6. Avoid becoming overweight, and limit your intake of fatty foods.

7. See a doctor if you notice a lump or observe a change in a mole, or abnormal bleeding.

8. See a doctor if you have persistent problems, such as a persistent cough, a persistent hoarseness, a change in bowel habits or an unexplained weight loss.

9. Have a cervical smear regularly.

10. Check your breasts regularly, and if possible undergo mammography at regular intervals above the age of 50.

B.4 The Government's overall, long-term objective is a reduction in both the mortality and morbidity caused by all cancers. With present knowledge the Government believes that there are four cancers for which it is now sensible to set specific outcome targets: breast, cervical, skin and lung cancers.

OBJECTIVES

To reduce ill-health and death caused by breast and cervical cancer.

To reduce ill-health and death caused by skin cancers – by increasing awareness of the need to avoid excessive skin exposure to ultra-violet light.

To reduce ill-health and death caused by lung cancer – and other conditions associated with tobacco use – by reducing smoking prevalence and tobacco consumption throughout the population.

MAIN TARGETS

(a) Breast Cancer

> **A.** **To reduce the death rate for breast cancer in the population invited for screening by at least 25% by the year 2000 (from 95.1 per 100,000 population in 1990 to no more than 71.3 per 100,000).**

B.5 More women die from breast cancer in England than from any other form of cancer. Although different therapies are being assessed in an attempt to define optimal treatment for the disease once diagnosed, early detection is of paramount importance. It is vital, therefore, that women be aware of their breasts and report any unusual changes to their doctor immediately.

B.6 The United Kingdom became the first country within the European Community to launch a nationwide breast cancer screening programme using a computerised call and recall system. Women aged 50-64 are being invited to be screened every three years, and older women may be screened three yearly on request. All women aged between 50 and 64 who are registered with a GP should have been invited for mammography by 1993. Successful screening detects the disease at a stage when there is scope for effective treatment.

B.7 Abnormalities detected by mammography are investigated further at specialist assessment centres. The combination of expertly trained staff, new equipment and an effective call and recall system has proved highly successful. Early figures from the programme suggest that it is more accurate and detects more cancers than originally predicted. In addition, a higher number of women than expected are accepting their screening invitations. In order to encourage participation, particularly by women from black and ethnic minority groups, the Government has funded a pilot programme to improve uptake of both breast and cervical cancer screening by these groups.

B.8 The aim of the programme is to reduce breast cancer deaths in the population invited for screening by at least 25% by the year 2000, compared to 1990. This should save some 1,250 lives per year. **The Government believes that the priority for this area should be the maintenance of the high standards achieved so far in the programme, and the encouragement of women to take up screening invitations.**

(b) Cervical Cancer

B.9 Unlike breast cancer, cervical cancer can be prevented before it starts. Changes sometimes take place in the cells of the cervix which in time may lead to cancer. Smear tests can detect the abnormal cells which might eventually become cancerous. Straightforward treatment to the cervix at this stage can prevent the disease. It is for this reason that cervical screening forms an important part of the Government's strategy to combat cancer. Although deaths from cervical cancer have fallen gradually over the last 20 years more than 1,500 women still die of the disease each year. Overseas evidence suggests that effective cervical screening could reduce deaths amongst women screened by over 80%.

> **B.** To reduce the incidence of invasive cervical cancer by at least 20% by the year 2000 (from 15 per 100,000 population in 1986 to no more than 12 per 100,000).

B.10 Cervical screening was first introduced in the NHS in the 1960s. **In 1988 the Government introduced a national cervical cancer screening programme using computerised call and recall systems.** Health authorities are required to invite women aged 20-64 for cervical screening, and to recall them at least every five years. All women in that group should have been invited for screening by April 1993.

B.11 Women over 65 are not automatically invited for cancer screening, but they will be invited for cervical screening if their previous two cervical smears have not been negative.

B.12 The Government believes that the priority for this area must be the continued development of good practice in operating the screening programme, and in encouraging women to be screened.

(c) **Skin Cancer**

> **C.** To halt the year-on-year increase in the incidence of skin cancer by 2005.

B.13 The number of cases of skin cancer (non-melanotic cancer and malignant melanoma) has been rising in recent years, unlike some other forms of cancer. On the latest available information, there are about 28,000 cases of skin cancers a year and about 1,500 deaths. The main risk factor which is believed to account for the increase in incidence is the increased extent to which people expose themselves to the sun, and to sunbeds, and thus to the ultra-violet radiation which is thought to cause the majority of skin cancers.

B.14 The incidence of these cancers is likely to increase further over the next few years, as these cancers often take several years to develop and past exposure to the sun will result in cancers continuing to develop in the future. The Government's aim is to halt this increase as soon as possible.

B.15 The main change which is required to achieve this is an alteration in individuals' attitudes to sun exposure, and an improvement in their understanding of skin cancer and the relevant risk factors. Copies of a leaflet "Are you Dying to Get a Sun Tan" were distributed by the Pharmacy Health Care Scheme in 1991, and the Health Education Authority provides additional guidance. This work needs to be built upon, to increase the numbers of people who are aware of their own skin type and, in the light of that knowledge, avoid excessive exposure to the sun for themselves and their children.

B.16 At the same time it is important that the sun and the risks of skin cancer are seen in perspective. Unlike the risk factors for some other cancers, there are positive benefits of being outside on sunny days: ranging from the feeling of relaxation and well-being that this produces, to the prevention of rickets especially in members of some ethnic groups and the elderly. The emphasis should be on sensible levels of exposure to the sun.

B.17 The Government will thus develop a strategy to increase awareness of skin cancer and how to reduce each individual's risk, through public information and awareness activity.

(d) Lung Cancer

Lung cancer, smoking and other diseases

B.18 At least 80% of lung cancer is associated with smoking, some 26,000 deaths a year. On top of this, the habit kills more than twice as many people from other diseases. It has been estimated that among an average 1,000 young adults who smoke cigarettes regularly; about one will be murdered, about six will be killed on the roads, but about 250 will be killed before their time by tobacco. Despite the substantial fall in smoking prevalence over the last twenty years, smoking remains the largest single cause of preventable mortality in England.

Smoking cessation

B.19 To achieve the objective it will be necessary that new smokers are not recruited to the habit and also that those who already smoke are able to stop. Former smokers live longer than those who continue to smoke: the risk of death compared with that for continuing smokers begins to decline shortly after giving up until after some 15 years of abstinence it returns almost to that of those who have never smoked. Giving up smoking greatly reduces the risk of dying from cancer. For lung cancer a 30 to 50% reduction after 10 years' abstinence has been reported.

Environmental tobacco smoke ("Passive Smoking")

B.20 Although the vast majority of tobacco-related lung cancer deaths occur in smokers, of the order of several hundred lung cancer deaths each year may occur in non-smokers as a result of inhaling environmental tobacco smoke over many years. Exposure to environmental tobacco smoke has also been linked with respiratory illness in infants and young children.

Smoking in pregnancy

B.21 If women can be helped to give up smoking before, or in the early stages of pregnancy, and remain non-smokers, there will be significant health benefits to both the babies and the mothers. There is considerable evidence to link smoking in pregnancy with increased fetal and neonatal mortality and low birthweight, and also evidence of an association with delayed physical and mental development of children. Success in this group will also help reduce smoking prevalence amongst women aged 16 to 24 where special attention is needed since prevalence is not falling as in other groups.

> **D.** **To reduce the death rate for lung cancer by at least 30% in men under 75 and 15% in women under 75 by 2010 (from 60 per 100,000 for men and 24.1 per 100,000 for women in 1990 to no more than 42 and 20.5 respectively).**

> **E.** **To reduce the prevalence of cigarette smoking in men and women aged 16 and over to no more than 20% by the year 2000 (a reduction of at least 35% in men and 29% in women, from a prevalence in 1990 of 31% and 28% respectively).**
>
> **F.** **In addition to the overall reduction in prevalence, at least a third of women smokers to stop smoking at the start of their pregnancy by the year 2000.**
>
> **G.** **To reduce the consumption of cigarettes by at least 40% by the year 2000 (from 98 billion manufactured cigarettes per year in 1990 to 59 bn.).**
>
> **H.** **To reduce smoking prevalence among 11-15 year olds by at least 33% by 1994 (from about 8% in 1988 to less than 6%).**

Notes on targets

Target D   In view of the time lag for reduction in lung cancer, these targets will reflect smoking prevalence during the 1990s. The different reductions for men and women reflect the fact that the trend in lung cancer deaths for men is already coming down, unlike that for women, and also that over previous decades more men than women smokers have given up. In addition there are different trends in different age groups which will need to be monitored closely. The target represents an estimate of the minimum likely to be achieved should smoking prevalence targets be met.

Target E   The information with which to monitor progress is currently available every two years from the General Household Survey.

Target F   Results from the 1985 Infant Feeding Survey indicated that 39% of mothers smoked before pregnancy, and of these a quarter gave up at some point during their pregnancy.

Target G   Stopping smoking is the most effective way of reducing the health risks from smoking. However, the more a person smokes the greater the health risks. To encourage those who remain smokers to cut down, the consumption target is designed to be more challenging than that implied by the prevalence targets. Regular data are available from the HM Customs and Excise.

Target H   The target quoted is that of the Health Education Authority's Teenage Smoking programme. It is monitored by surveys conducted by Office of the Population, Censuses and Surveys (OPCS). Longer term targets will need to be considered at the end of the programme.

Figure 12

Death rates for Lung Cancer

England 1970-1990* and target for the year 2010
Males aged under 75°

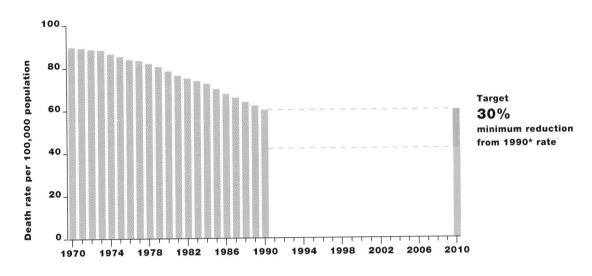

Source: OPCS (ICD 162)

Death rates for Lung Cancer

England 1970-1990* and target for the year 2010
Females aged under 75°

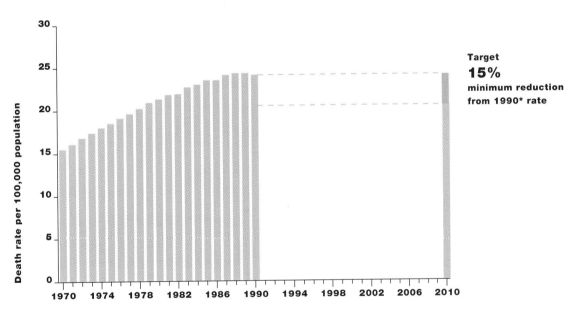

Source: OPCS (ICD 162)

* Rates are calculated using a 3 year average plotted against the middle year of average

° Rates are calculated using the European Standard Population to take into account differences in age structure

B.22 *Figure 12* shows the death rate for lung cancer, and the targets.

B.23 Predictions of future trends are hard to make and are subject to wide error. It cannot be assumed that current trends in the reduction of smoking prevalence will necessarily continue, since the smokers that remain are likely to be the heavier and more dependent ones who find it hard to give up. Considerable effort will therefore be required even to maintain present trends. However, the Government believes that it is right to aim for targets in this key aspect of health which are significantly in excess of current trends.

B.24 In the end, the decision of whether or not to smoke is a matter of individual choice, although this is influenced by many factors, not least – for those who already smoke – the fact that nicotine is addictive. There is much that can be done to support individuals by giving them information, advice and practical help. Prevalence of cigarette smoking is affected by many, often inter-related factors including:

- uptake of smoking amongst young people
- price and income
- health education
- controls on smoking in public places
- controls on advertising and promotion
- public attitudes to smoking.

B.25 The overall target for reducing smoking, and therefore lung cancer, will be achieved in part by existing smokers stopping, and in part by other people choosing not to take up the habit. In older age groups reductions will principally come through stopping, whereas reductions in younger age groups will largely reflect success in lowering the numbers of young people who start to smoke. Strategies need to take both aspects into account.

i.   Government

B.26 The Government will develop a comprehensive strategy to reduce both smoking prevalence and the consumption of tobacco amongst those who cannot stop smoking. An interdepartmental task force will be

created to develop and implement this strategy. Action will focus on the following areas:

Price

B.27 The real price of tobacco products has risen by 43% over the last 12 years. Progress on smoking would be undermined if the real price of tobacco were to fall. **The Government will therefore undertake at least to maintain the real level of taxes on tobacco products. In addition, the Government will work with the European Community to encourage other European countries with prices lower than those in the United Kingdom to raise them to match our own.**

Health education

B.28 The United Kingdom is internationally recognised as a world leader in health education about smoking. It is accepted that effective health education has played a significant role in the United Kingdom's success in reducing levels of smoking. In schools, the National Curriculum now requires children between 7 and 16 to be taught about the harmful effects of smoking.

- **Existing national programmes on teenage smoking and smoking and pregnancy will be continued and, where possible, expanded. The teenage programme has received an increase in funding of £0.5 million for this financial year.**

- **In addition, the Department of Health and the Health Education Authority will develop proposals for a major health education programme on smoking aimed at adults.** The programme will need to focus on groups at particular risk such as young adult women and unskilled workers.

Protecting non-smoking members of the public

B.29 In December of last year the Department of the Environment, with the other Departments concerned, issued comprehensive guidance on controlling smoking in public places, with the aim that at least 80% of public places should be covered by effective policies by 1994. Considerable progress has been made already, and the Government will build on this.

- **Schemes will be developed to monitor the provision of smoke-free areas.**

B.30 The Government believes that the voluntary approach has many advantages in this area. But if the satisfactory progress already made does not continue it will consider statutory means to protect non-smoking members of the public in public places. If necessary, enabling legislation will be introduced for this purpose.

B.31 Enabling legislation already exists to control and ban smoking from most forms of public transport and this has been increasingly invoked in recent years. The vast majority of public transport in England is now either completely smoke-free or has limited separate provision for smokers. To add to this **the Department of Transport will seek an opportunity to amend the relevant legislation to enable taxi drivers to ban smoking in their cabs.**

Controls on tobacco advertising and promotion

B.32 Successive Governments have effectively controlled tobacco advertising and promotion through a system of voluntary agreements, and a tough new agreement was announced last year. This Government believes that such agreements continue to represent the best way of controlling tobacco advertising, but recognises that there is widespread concern that such controls should be strong and effective. **It therefore proposes to review the effects of tobacco advertising, particularly on children, and consider what further steps are necessary.**

Other steps

B.33 The Government will also pursue the following policies to limit the effects of tobacco use.

- **Any novel tobacco products which come to the attention of the Government will be rapidly assessed. If there is sufficient medical** evidence of harmful effects, steps will be taken to ban their use in this country.

- The Department of Health will maintain its careful scrutiny of modifications (and possible modifications) to tobacco products and will set up a review to consider whether the use of additives and emission of toxic substances from cigarettes should be controlled by legislation.

- The Department of Health will provide advice to insurance companies on the health effects of smoking and encourage them to consider whether they should introduce or extend preferential treatment to non-smokers.

B.34 The Government's policy towards its own employees is that Departments should adopt smoking policies to protect non-smokers from tobacco smoke in the working environment. Government Departments will work to establish such policies on their own premises, with guidance on health aspects of smoking from the Civil Service Occupational Health Service. Local government has a key role in implementing national guidance on smoking in public places and in the workplace. Local authorities should ensure that all their premises (particularly educational establishments) are covered by appropriate no-smoking policies.

ii. Non-statutory organisations

B.35 The two major voluntary organisations which aim to reduce smoking, ASH (Action on Smoking and Health) and QUIT, will need to continue to play a leading role in disseminating information, encouraging action by others, and providing advice and support. The Government will encourage other voluntary organisations concerned with the promotion of health to ensure that the health hazards of smoking are given adequate weight.

iii. The National Health Service

B.36 The NHS has a key role in advising people against smoking, and in helping them to stop. Amongst further developments the Government will seek are:

- **patients being asked routinely about their smoking habits – GPs will be encouraged to record quantified information on patient smoking habits, which can then be aggregated in practice profiles**

- **an increase in the numbers of smokers visiting their GPs who receive smoking cessation advice either opportunistically or in separate clinics**

- **an increase in the smoking cessation advice given to smokers attending hospital out-patient clinics**

- **a high priority given to the provision of advice on smoking and support for those wishing to stop**

- **an increase in the smoking cessation advice given to pregnant women attending hospital and GP antenatal clinics, with support for those wishing to stop.**

B.37 In addition, the whole of the health service will need to work towards a virtually smoke-free environment for staff, patients and visitors as rapidly as possible. Managers and professional staff will need to ensure that advice and support is available for those working in the NHS who wish to stop smoking. The individual professions within the health service should consider what more can be done to educate and encourage those of their members who remain smokers. The NHS should develop an exemplary role, leading the way for other employers to follow, including:

- **stopping all sales of tobacco on NHS premises except to long-stay patients who are smokers, by the end of 1992**

- **ensuring that the NHS is smoke-free except for limited necessary provision of separate smoking rooms by 31 May 1993.**

iv. Employers

B.38 Those employers who do not have no-smoking policies should urgently consider how to introduce them, in the light of guidance issued by the Health and Safety Executive, and also what support they can offer to those employees who wish to stop smoking. No-smoking policies not only contribute to the individual health of both smoking and non-smoking employees, but may also reduce fire risks and operational costs. **The aim should be that the large majority of employees are covered by a no-smoking policy by 1995.**

v. Retail tobacconists

B.39 The Government wishes to see illegal sales of tobacco to children under 16 eliminated. All retailers must recognise that selling tobacco to children is unlawful. The Government will monitor the working of those parts of recent legislation which strengthened the arrangements for enforcing the law and for bringing successful prosecutions against retailers who break the law.

vi. The media

B.40 The media can play a key role in publicising the health consequences of smoking. Producers and editors will need carefully to consider how they portray smoking in order to ensure that the habit is not promoted.

vii. Individuals

B.41 The choices made by individuals and groups of individuals will ultimately determine whether targets are met. Whether to smoke is a matter of individual choice, but in deciding whether to continue to smoke current smokers need to consider the potentially devastating consequences of their habit both for themselves, their loved ones and others who are forced to inhale the smoke they produce.

VARIATIONS

B.42 As with CHD and stroke, there are significant variations in death rates from cancers. For lung and cervical cancer, rates are generally higher in the north of the country and amongst people in manual occupational groups. Unusually, this pattern is reversed for breast cancer. Differences are also seen for cancer rates amongst black and ethnic minority groups. For example, rates higher than in the white population have been seen for cancer of the gall bladder in people originating from the Caribbean and Indian sub-continent, whilst they have lower rates for cancer of the lung and stomach. There is also evidence that, as with other preventive services, there are differences in uptake of screening both by occupational and by ethnic group.

B.43 Smoking prevalence also varies between different parts of the country and different groups. For example, people in manual groups are more likely to smoke than non-manual. Amongst black and ethnic minority groups, smoking prevalence is lower than the white population in people of Afro-Caribbean origin and in people of Asian origin. There are however examples where rates are higher. Given the importance of smoking in a wide variety of diseases, a reduction in smoking amongst groups of people with high prevalence could be expected to have a significant effect in reducing overall variations in health.

CONSEQUENTIAL IMPROVEMENTS IN HEALTH

B.44 In addition to reductions in lung cancer deaths, achievement of the proposed smoking prevalence and consumption targets should lead to improvements in a range of conditions including cancer of the mouth, pharynx, larynx, oesophagus, pancreas, bladder and other organs, coronary heart disease, peripheral vascular disease, chronic bronchitis and other chronic obstructive airways diseases.

SECTION C

MENTAL ILLNESS

INTRODUCTION

C.1 Mental illness is a leading cause of illness and disability. It accounts for about 14% of certificated sickness absence, 14% of NHS inpatient costs and 4% of NHS pharmaceutical costs. The cost in human misery and suffering to individuals and their families is incalculable. *Figure 13* illustrates estimates of the prevalence of mental disorders in the population. Most common are illnesses such as depression and anxiety. Less common, but more severe, are the psychotic illnesses such as schizophrenia and affective psychosis.

Estimated frequency of mental disorders in the adult population over 16

Figure 13

MENTAL DISORDER	Point prevalence (percentage of the population over 16)	Lifetime risk (percentage of the population over 16)
Schizophrenia	0.2 - 0.5%	0.7 - 0.9%
Affective psychosis	0.1 - 0.5%	1%
Depressive disorder	3 - 6%	>20%
Anxiety states	2 - 7%	
Dementia (over age 65)	5%	
(over age 80)	20%	

C.2 Mental illness also leads to many deaths from higher rates of physical illness and from suicide. There were 5,567 deaths from suicide (and undetermined injury) in 1991 in England. Trends in suicides differ by age and sex (see *figure 14*). There is a particularly worrying rise in younger men.

Figure 14

Death rates for Suicide and Undetermined Injury

by age   England 1969-1991*

Males

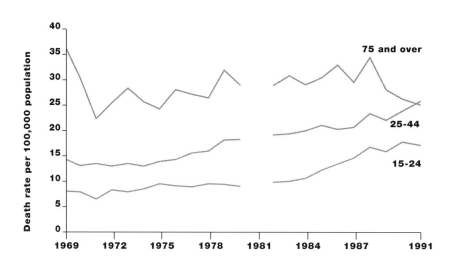

Females

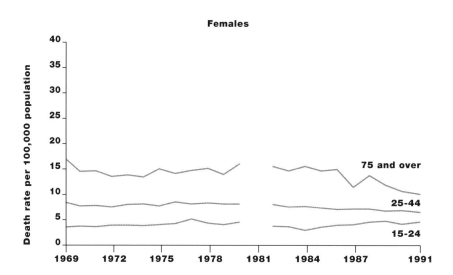

Source: OPCS (ICD E950:E959 + E980:E989)

*Data for 1981 were affected by industrial action by registrars and are excluded

C.3 Elderly people are a vulnerable group. Severe mental illness is as prevalent in elderly people as in younger people, and depression is more common in the elderly than in any other age group. Dementia is a chronic and progressively disabling condition mainly occurring in elderly people.

C.4 The mental health of children and adolescents is a particularly important area as many are vulnerable to physical, intellectual, emotional, social or behavioural developmental disorders which, if not treated, may have serious implications for adult life.

C.5 Mentally disordered people who commit offences are also a particularly vulnerable group. There is a risk that if their health and social care needs are not recognised and met, they may slip into a vicious circle of imprisonment, re-offending and deteriorating mental health.

C.6 The risk factors for mental illness are multiple. They include genetic factors and aspects of the physical and social environments. There is acknowledged scope for improvement through more effective diagnosis, treatment and rehabilitation. The contributory causes of suicide are by no means fully understood and research is continuing to elucidate the role of factors such as life events and access to means of suicide.

C.7 In addition, family life, education, housing and employment all influence psychological health, and many agencies other than the NHS and local authority social services departments can make a significant contribution. Strategies need also to exploit the potential of the voluntary and private sectors and to take account of the views of users and carers. Essential support is provided by carers and their own needs for support must be recognised. Mental illness, more than many other illnesses, has been the subject of immense stigma and discrimination, and much can be done by the media, for example, to improve this situation.

OBJECTIVE
To reduce ill-health and death caused by mental illness

C.8 This will require an appropriate balance of prevention, treatment and rehabilitation and the development of services and practice in both primary and secondary care, as well as action outside the health and social services.

MAIN TARGETS

> **A.   To improve significantly the health and social functioning of mentally ill people.**
>
> **B.   To reduce the overall suicide rate by at least 15% by the year 2000 (from 11.1 per 100,000 population in 1990 to no more than 9.4).**
>
> **C.   To reduce the suicide rate of severely mentally ill people by at least 33% by the year 2000 (from the estimate of 15% in 1990 to no more than 10%).**

Notes on targets

> *Target A* Initially the focus will be on the severely mentally ill, with the scope of the target being extended over time to include the less severely mentally ill.
>
> *Targets B–C* The targets include both suicides and undetermined deaths.

C.9 The death rates for suicide and undetermined injuries, together with the suicide target, are shown at *figure 15*. As with other Key Areas, considerably more data are available for the mortality that results from mental illness than for morbidity. However, the major burden is one of morbidity. It is unfortunate, therefore, that limitations of current data mean that it is not feasible at present to set targets for morbidity.

C.10 The Government proposes in the short term to set *quantified* targets for reducing suicide but an *unquantified* one for improving health and social functioning. A high priority will be to develop the means to replace the latter with quantified targets. Setting quantified targets for suicide does not mean that they will be the sole or primary focus of attention. The professional and service developments which will be necessary to progress towards the suicide targets will also have a broad beneficial effect on health and social functioning.

C.11 This approach is wider than that of the Green Paper, which took as its primary target the substantial completion of transfer of services away from large hospitals to a balanced range of locally based services. Such development of locally based services has long been Government policy and remains so. It will be fundamental to the achievement of mental illness targets. However, the Government was encouraged by the consultation process to believe that in setting targets it should adopt a more wide-ranging approach as set out here.

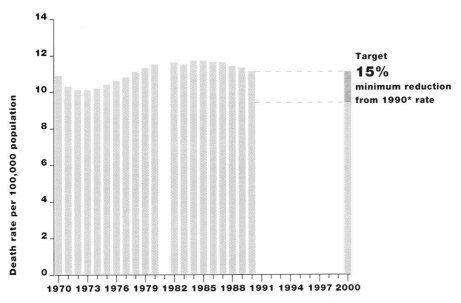

Death rates for Suicide and Undetermined Injury

Figure 15

England 1970-1990*• and target for the year 2000
All persons°

* Rates are calculated using a 3 year average plotted against the middle year of the average

• Data for 1981 were affected by industrial action by registrars and are excluded, thus rates for 1980 and 1982 are based on two year averages

° Rates are calculated using the European Standard Population to take into account differences in age structure

Source: OPCS (ICD E950:E959+E980:E989)

C.12 Success in meeting targets for improving the health and social functioning of mentally ill people will mostly be achieved by continuing developments in the services provided by the NHS, social services and others.

C.13 There is much, too, that health and social services can do to detect and prevent suicide. Most people who commit suicide have recently been in contact with a health professional, usually a GP, which means that there are opportunities for prevention and treatment which are not currently being identified. To this end the Government, in co-operation with the relevant professional bodies, will promote initiatives to increase professionals' awareness and expertise in identifying, assessing and treating people who are in danger of harming themselves. This will include the improvement of clinical auditing of suicides; the preparation and dissemination of clinical guidelines; and the introduction of specific training courses for GPs and specialist mental health care professionals.

C.14 Achieving targets will require:

- the improvement of information and understanding
- the development of comprehensive local services
- the further development of good practice.

(a) Improving information and understanding

C.15 The principal obstacles to setting national targets for health and social functioning of mentally ill people are limitations of available data and inconsistencies in the use of instruments to measure functioning. The Government believes however that it should be possible to set such outcome targets both nationally and locally by 1995, and there are four principal steps that can be taken to achieve this.

- **The Government is developing proposals with a view to commissioning a survey to establish national baseline data on population prevalence of mental illness (subject to feasibility).**

- **All providers of psychiatric services, including NHS Trusts, will be encouraged to use (on a sample basis at specified intervals) brief standardised assessment procedures of symptom state, social disability and quality of life.**

The Government will work with appropriate professional bodies to develop such procedures and any relevant training programmes for introduction nationally in 1994/5. Sites for piloting will be identified during 1992/3.

- **Health Authorities should specify in contracts that mental health teams should introduce local multidisciplinary audit of all suicides (and undetermined deaths) of mentally ill people in contact with specialist mental health services during 1993/4.**

   This will be supported by the Confidential Inquiry into deaths by homicide or suicide by mentally ill people, in which the Royal College of Psychiatrists is playing a leading role. Similarly, suicides of people who are not in touch with the specialist mental health teams should in time be audited by the primary care team.

- **There will need to be improved supervision of patients' care in the community.**

   Most, if not all, seriously mentally ill people who commit suicide are in contact with specialist services. Accurate up-to-date records of those people in the community who have care programmes are a prerequisite. The Government is currently funding a study to evaluate progress in the implementation of the Care Programme Approach.

(b)   Developing comprehensive local services

C.16 If targets are to be achieved, there will need to be continued development and improvements in comprehensive local services for all mental illness, in consultation with users of services. Attention needs to be paid to illnesses not only in adults (including elderly people), but also in children and adolescents.

- **All Provider Units should have effective systems for collecting and using data about service contacts by 1995.**

   Systems will need to be developed locally to identify people who are in danger of losing contact with services and to assist in preventing them from falling through the 'care network'.

- **All District Health Authorities, Family Health Service Authorities, local authorities and relevant voluntary bodies will need to establish joint mechanisms for purchasing local services, including supported housing, and for ensuring that they deliver continuity of health and social care.**

- **Regional Health Authorities should take the lead where necessary in promoting the development of a strategic framework by 1994/5 for the development of comprehensive locally based services to replace dependence on inappropriate provision in large outdated institutions within a realistic timetable. A national task force is being established, including officers from the relevant statutory agencies, to further the development of locally based services. There is much to be learned from Districts that have already made this transition.**

(c)   Continuing development of good practice

C.17 The Government will work with professional, voluntary and other bodies to identify and promote good practice. Aspects of good practice will include the following:

- **Primary health care teams and local secondary health care services will need to develop local good practice guidelines for the assessment and management of common psychiatric conditions, events and emergencies and for the use of the Mental Health Act.**

  The Government will continue to work with the Royal Colleges of Psychiatrists, of General Practitioners, of Nursing and other professional bodies to encourage the continued development of consensus statements of good practice.

- **Multidisciplinary secondary care teams should provide comprehensive services, including:**

family intervention services

direct education of users

education and support to carers of people with a severe mental illness, including dementia

genetic counselling if requested.

- **Training for primary care teams, social workers, day and home care staff, casualty staff and hospital and community doctors and nurses is necessary to help them improve their recognition and assessment of depression, anxiety and suicidal risk, and to manage them appropriately.**

The Department of Health is funding a senior GP Fellow at the Royal College of General Practitioners, in collaboration with the Mental Health Foundation and the Gatsby Charitable Trust, to take a national lead on continuing GP education in mental illness, with the task of expediting the education of the primary health care team in this area.

- **Complementary services by voluntary agencies which support and educate mentally ill people and their carers should be promoted locally.**

- **Local support for voluntary agencies, such as those that support people at high risk for depression, should be improved in order to strengthen the role that they play.**

- **Prevention strategies should be implemented in the workplace.**

C.18 On this last, the Health and Safety Commission have already convened a formal working party involving the Government, employers, trades unions and others on mental health at work, which will advise on strategies and good practice. The Department of Health and the Confederation of British Industry have recently sponsored a conference on mental health, a report of which will be published by HMSO during 1992.

(d) Mentally disordered offenders

C.19 The essential task here is to ensure that mentally disordered offenders who need specialist health and social care are diverted from the criminal justice system as early as possible. This requires close co-operation between all the local agencies concerned. **Authorities' strategic and purchasing plans should include the necessary range of health and social services (both secure and non-secure) to enable them to respond to these people's special needs.**

C.20 Diversion schemes have already been introduced in a number of areas with help from Home Office funding or through local inter-agency initiatives. Additional Government funding over the next three years will be available to promote psychiatric assessment schemes linked to the courts. These and other approaches will be further developed in the light of the current review of services for mentally disordered offenders being carried out by the Department of Health and the Home Office. In addition, the Home Office is introducing major changes to the organisation of health services in prisons and is giving particular attention to the mental health care needs of prisoners.

(e) Benzodiazepines

C.21 Benzodiazepines (minor tranquillisers such as diazepam) are widely prescribed for depression and anxiety. However, they do not usually represent the best treatment as they are not curative, and there is a high risk of dependency. They are not suitable for long-term treatment of depression and anxiety. Further effort is needed to review use of benzodiazepines and replace them, as necessary, with behavioural, cognitive and other psychotherapeutic methods of treatment and, if appropriate, antidepressants.

C.22 Given the potential for better forms of treatment, the rate of prescription of benzodiazepines (particularly repeat prescription and prescriptions to elderly people) for depression and anxiety continues to be a major concern, despite falling significantly in recent years.

C.23 Progress on this will depend greatly on the leadership of the professional organisations representing GPs, in collaboration with the Royal Colleges of Psychiatrists and Physicians. In addition to the general continued development of good practice possible action would include:

- improving education of primary care teams about non-prescribing interventions in the management of anxiety disorders and in graded withdrawal of benzodiazepines in chronic users

- including benzodiazepine prescribing habits in medical audit of general practice.

VARIATIONS

C.24 Patterns of mental illness, like physical illness, show variations between different parts of the population. Suicide for example, is more common among men in manual than non-manual groups. There are also striking gender and age differences in suicide. Rates of suicide are higher in men than women, whereas the reverse applies to parasuicide.

C.25 There are also significant variations in utilisation of psychiatric services in different areas and between ethnic and socio-economic groups of the population. In many instances it is still not entirely clear how much these reflect true variations in morbidity, or to what extent they are due to other factors, for example related to the provision of services.

CONSEQUENTIAL IMPROVEMENTS IN HEALTH

C.26 It is known that physical and mental disorders often exist together and aggravate each other. For example, severely mentally ill people have extremely high rates of death from cancers, respiratory and cardiovascular disease. As well as indicating the need for improved physical health care, this could be due to shared risk factors, or because the presence of one type of illness increases the risk of developing others. In either case, success in reducing the burdens associated with mental illnesses may assist in reducing those associated with physical illnesses, and *vice versa*.

C.27 Action to achieve targets for reducing excessive alcohol consumption will have a more direct benefit. Excessive drinking is associated with depression, anxiety, eating disorders, and personality problems. Ten per cent of psychiatric inpatients have an alcohol problem. There are high rates of suicide among people with alcohol problems and alcohol intoxication is involved in up to 65% of suicide attempts.

SECTION D

HIV/AIDS AND SEXUAL HEALTH

INTRODUCTION

D.1 Good personal and sexual relationships can actively promote health and well-being. On the other hand, sexual activity can sometimes lead to unwanted pregnancies, ill-health or disease. The advent of HIV and AIDS has highlighted a number of health and social problems which centre on sexual activity. This has made it easier to talk about such problems and also much more important to do so. HIV infection is perhaps the greatest new public health challenge this century. It is a new disease, and because it may not produce symptoms for many years after infection there is a need to develop increasingly effective ways of monitoring its incidence and prevalence in the population.

D.2 HIV is primarily sexually transmitted and prevention of infection depends largely upon changes in sexual behaviour. There are risks associated with multiple sexual partners. Safer sexual practices, including the use of condoms to reduce the risk of infection, must be encouraged. Because AIDS can develop many years after infection, its incidence is a poor indicator of recent changes in sexual behaviour. Other sexually transmitted diseases (STDs), particularly gonorrhoea, are better early markers of such changes. These diseases are themselves a cause of significant ill-health.

D.3 Sexual health is not however restricted to the control of disease. It also encompasses family planning and family planning services, which play an important part in the health of children and the well-being of families by reducing the number of unwanted pregnancies and births.

HIV/AIDS

D.4 The Acquired Immune Deficiency Syndrome (AIDS) is caused by infection with the Human Immunodeficiency Virus (HIV). HIV is transmitted through penetrative sexual intercourse; by infected blood (principally through drug users sharing contaminated injecting equipment); and from an infected mother to her baby before or during childbirth, or through breast milk. Worldwide, the most common mode of transmission is heterosexual intercourse. Evidence suggests that most of those infected with HIV will eventually develop AIDS, and about half will do so within ten years. No cure for AIDS is yet available.

D.5 The cumulative total of AIDS cases reported in England by the end of March 1992 stood at 5,366, of whom 3,336 had died. Up to March 1992, 15,133 cases of HIV infection had been reported in England. The actual number of people who have become infected, many of them unaware of it, is certainly higher. Homosexual and bisexual men still account for the greatest numbers of reports of both HIV and AIDS. The numbers infected heterosexually are much smaller but the fastest rate of growth is now seen in this group.

D.6 The Government attaches a high priority to obtaining better information about the incidence and prevalence of HIV in the population. In 1990 it began a programme of anonymised HIV surveys. Initial results showed a prevalence of 1 in 500 amongst women attending certain antenatal clinics in inner London. Rates elsewhere were much lower. Amongst men attending certain inner London genito-urinary medicine (GUM) clinics there was a prevalence of 1 in 5 for homosexual and bisexual men, and 1 in 100 for heterosexual men.

Other sexually transmitted diseases
D.7 Cases of gonorrhoea have shown a declining trend in recent years. GUM clinics have played an important part in achieving this, through early diagnosis and treatment of those with symptoms and also of their (often symptomless) partners. However, the trend has not continued over the last two years. A total of 19,086 cases was reported in 1990 compared to 18,738 cases in 1988, and this was mainly due to a slight increase in cases in males in both 1989 and 1990. This underlines the need for continuing publicity and education about sexual health.

D.8 Gonorrhoea and other STDs are themselves a major cause of ill-health, and can have long-term consequences such as infertility, ectopic pregnancy and genital cancers. In addition, current research suggests that some STDs may facilitate the transmission of HIV.

Family planning

D.9 The Government is concerned at evidence which shows that some parents, had they been better informed, would not have started down the path to parenthood at the time they did. In the Chief Medical Officer's Annual Report for 1990 it was estimated that almost half of all conceptions were in some sense unwanted or unintended.

D.10 By no means all unintended or unwanted pregnancies result in unwanted babies, but there is clearly a need for better access for everyone to family planning information and services. The health benefits from this would be significant, even if not easily measurable, and there could also be important social and resource benefits.

OBJECTIVES

To reduce the incidence of HIV infection

To reduce the incidence of other sexually transmitted diseases

To develop further and strengthen monitoring and surveillance

To provide effective services for diagnosis and treatment of HIV and other STDs

To reduce the number of unwanted pregnancies

To ensure the provision of effective family planning services for those people who want them

THE HEALTH OF THE NATION

MAIN TARGETS

> **A. To reduce the incidence of gonorrhoea among men and women aged 15-64 by at least 20% by 1995 (from 61 new cases per 100,000 population in 1990 to no more than 49 new cases per 100,000).**
>
> **B. To reduce the rate of conceptions amongst the under 16s by at least 50% by the year 2000 (from 9.5 per 1,000 girls aged 13-15 in 1989 to no more than 4.8).**

> **C. To reduce the percentage of injecting drug misusers who report sharing injecting equipment in the previous four weeks by at least 50% by 1997, and by at least a further 50% by the year 2000 (from 20% in 1990 to no more than 10% by 1997 and no more than 5% by the year 2000).**

Notes on targets

> *Target A* The level of this target reflects what is seen as feasible given the achievements in reducing reported cases of gonorrhoea during the last ten years. It will be monitored by routine data from GUM clinics.
>
> *Target B* There were 7,922 conceptions amongst under 16s in 1989 (the latest year for which figures are available). Progress on reducing pregnancy rates can be monitored through existing data, published by OPCS.
>
> *Target C* Information on the sharing of injecting equipment is available from surveys of drug misusers' risk-taking behaviour, undertaken periodically by a range of organisations.

D.11 *Figure 16* shows the trend in gonorrhoea cases, together with a target reduction of 20%. *Figure 17* shows conception rates amongst under 16s, together with the target for reduction.

Figure 16

New Cases of Gonorrhoea at GUM* Clinics

England 1980-1990 and target for the year 1995
All persons

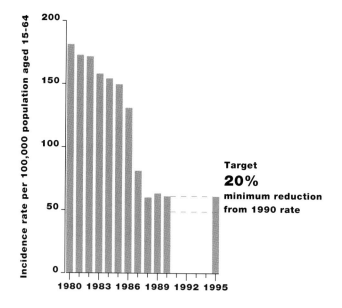

Source: Forms SBH60 and KC60 (from 1988)

* GUM=genito-urinary medicine

Figure 17

Conception Rates

England 1974-1989 and target for the year 2000
Females aged under 16 years of age

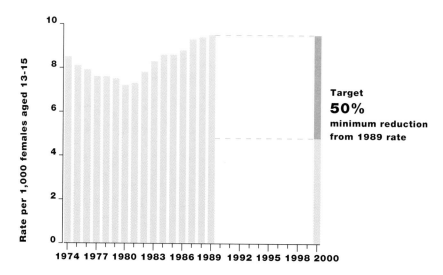

Source: OPCS Birth Statistics

D.12 The Government, health services, local authorities, the voluntary sector, the education sector and users of services will need to work together to meet these targets. There needs to be a willingness to address and discuss attitudes and behaviour in what are very sensitive areas.

(a) HIV and AIDS

D.13 If the spread of HIV infection is to be contained, behaviour change on a wide scale is needed. There is no single measure to overcome the threat that HIV poses to public health. A concerted campaign involving many different agencies is required. It is one of the strengths of the response to HIV in this and other countries that the threat has been met by considerable innovation and development in both the voluntary and statutory sectors.

D.14 For its part, the Government has developed a comprehensive five part strategy, co-ordinated across all Departments:

- **Prevention:** limiting the spread of HIV infection by encouraging behaviour change through public awareness campaigns and community-based initiatives, relevant education in schools and colleges, improved infection control procedures and improved prevention and treatment services for injecting drug misusers. National public education campaigns for the general public and specific sections of the community will continue to be developed by the Health Education Authority.

- **Monitoring, surveillance and research:** improving the understanding of the epidemiology of HIV infection, its transmission, natural history, and how HIV-related illness can be prevented and treated. The Department of Health liaises with other Government Departments on HIV and AIDS research.

- **Treatment, care and support:** ensuring the provision of diagnostic, treatment, care and support services in a co-ordinated way for the different groups of people with HIV and AIDS, according to their particular needs, and ensuring that professionals and volunteers are adequately and appropriately educated to care for these groups.

- **Social, legal and ethical issues:** fostering a climate of understanding and compassion, discouraging discrimination, and safeguarding confidentiality.

- **International co-operation:** fostering the full and continuing exchange of information between countries and discouraging coercive and discriminatory measures.

D.15 As part of this strategy the Government will continue to support local initiatives by health authorities, local authorities and voluntary organisations. The Government has set up an AIDS Action Group, chaired by a Department of Health Minister, to help achieve the most effective use of resources and disseminate information about good practice both locally and nationally.

(b) Other sexually transmitted diseases

D.16 The Monks Report[1] made a series of recommendations about manpower, training, resources and accommodation in GUM clinics. **Development of these services, and the establishment of easily accessible GUM provision for the residents of every district, should continue to be a priority within the NHS.**

(c) Drug misuse and HIV

D.17 Anonymised surveys of groups of injecting drugs misusers in London have shown that one in eight of those participating are HIV positive. Such people can transmit HIV infection to other drug misusers through the sharing of injecting equipment, and to drug misusers and others through unprotected sex.

D.18 The Government, health authorities, local authorities and others therefore need to continue to develop a comprehensive range of services to discourage drug misuse and to reduce risky behaviour such as injecting, sharing of equipment and unprotected sex. This will be achieved by making support and counselling, especially counselling on safer sexual practices, more available and accessible so that more users are brought into contact with such services. Health and local authorities will need to bear this in mind in agreeing contracts.

---

[1] A report published in November 1988 by a Working Group set up by the Department of Health to look into the workloads and organisation of GUM clinics. The report was accepted by the Government and disseminated widely throughout the NHS.

(d) Sex education in schools

D.19 The National Curriculum now requires pupils aged 11–14 to understand the processes of conception in human beings, know about the physical and emotional changes that take place during adolescence, and understand the need to have a responsible attitude to sexual behaviour. They must also now study the ways in which the healthy functioning of the human body may be affected by HIV.

D.20 Beyond this statutory requirement, schools' governing bodies are responsible for deciding whether any further sex education should be included in the school's curriculum, for maintaining a written record of that decision and, if they decide that additional sex education should be provided, for policy on its content and organisation. This gives schools a good deal of flexibility to take account of local circumstances and the views of parents. The Department for Education's guidance emphasises that schools have a clear responsibility to warn pupils of the health risks of casual and promiscuous sexual behaviour and to encourage pupils to have due regard to moral considerations, the value of family life and the responsibilities of parenthood.

(e) Family planning services

D.21 Family planning services span primary health care and hospital and community services. These services need to be complementary and balanced. District Health Authorities and Family Health Services Authorities need to work together and with other agencies to evaluate and develop existing services to meet the needs of those who use, or may wish to use, family planning services.

D.22 Regional Health Authorities (RHAs) are undertaking a comprehensive review of family planning services. To assist them in these reviews, the NHS Management Executive issued guidelines in January 1992 to RHAs giving advice on targeting services; service accessibility; information about services; sex education; and the particular needs of young people.

D.23 The aim is that by 1994/5 the full range of NHS family planning services, however provided, should be appropriate, accessible and comprehensive. There should be special provision for family planning and counselling services for young people which emphasise the importance of loving, stable personal relationships. The needs of other client groups where take-up is low should be addressed. Publicity should be used to increase public awareness of family planning services, including information about choice of doctor and the availability of emergency contraception. This should complement, and make use of, the education and information work undertaken nationally by the Family Planning Association with the support of the Health Education Authority.

D.24 The target for family planning relates to conceptions below the age of 16. Information about all unwanted pregnancies is difficult to collect, but it is reasonable to make the general assumption that pregnancies in those under 16 are not wanted. It is a matter of concern that the conception rate in those under 16 years of age is increasing. A package of measures which substantially reduces pregnancies in the under 16s may also be expected to exert a similar effect on unwanted pregnancies in those over 16.

VARIATIONS

D.25 Data on variations in the incidence and prevalence of HIV and other STDs need to be interpreted with caution. HIV can affect all parts of the community, though in England at present the majority of reports of HIV infection are among homosexual and bisexual men. For both HIV and other STDs there are greater numbers of reported cases in London than elsewhere, though this may in part reflect the existence of specialist services in London. Similarly, lower rates of STDs reported from GUM clinics in rural areas may reflect the greater use made in such areas of general practitioner services. As regards black and ethnic minority groups, the available data reflect the nature of the global epidemic with higher prevalence among people who have had links with parts of the world where prevalence is high.

D.26 As with other health promotion services there is some evidence of variations in rates of take-up of family planning services, though this evidence too must be interpreted with caution bearing in mind the availability of contraceptives from other sources. There is also evidence that suggests variations in the rates of unwanted pregnancies in different areas, with relatively more unwanted pregnancies in some inner-city areas, for example.

CONSEQUENTIAL IMPROVEMENTS IN HEALTH

D.27 The achievement of the target for gonorrhoea would reduce the burden of ill-health caused by its long-term consequences (such as infertility). It would also suggest that changes in sexual behaviour likely to reduce the prevalence of other STDs, including HIV, may have occurred. Although difficult to quantify, reductions in unwanted or unintended pregnancies can reduce risks to the health and well-being of women, their babies and their families.

SECTION E

ACCIDENTS

INTRODUCTION

E.1 Accidents are a major cause of death in England. They are the most common cause of death in people under 30 years. They are also a very important cause of illness and disability. Few accidents are due purely to chance. Many are preventable by information and education, and through measures like improved planning and design of the environment, education, better management in the workplace or greater vigilance and supervision in the home.

E.2 Considerable progress has already been made in reducing accidental injuries. Between 1981 and 1991 rates of death for all accidents fell by 23%. However, accidents still accounted for 10,193 deaths in England in 1991 of which 40% were motor vehicle traffic accidents and about 35% accidents in the home (see *figure 18*). The longstanding decline in accident mortality has halted among young adults. Less information is available about the injuries and disability resulting from accidents, but it is estimated that personal injuries as a result of road traffic accidents in England cost the nation approximately £4.5 billion in 1990 and that some 7% of total NHS expenditure results from accidental injuries.

E.3 Accidents take a particularly heavy toll on the lives of children. In 1991, 543 children under age 15 died as a result of accidents, making this the most common cause of death in children over 1 year. Accidents are also a significant cause of death and ill-health amongst elderly people. In 1991, 4,626 people aged over 65 died as a result of accidents.

E.4 In many accidents alcohol consumption is a significant contributory factor. Drugs, particularly benzodiazepines, and heightened emotional states generally may also play a part. In 1990, 9,500 drivers involved in road accidents in Great Britain who were tested for alcohol had exceeded the legal limit (compared to 13,400 in 1980).

Figure 18

Deaths from Accidents
All ages* England and Wales 1990

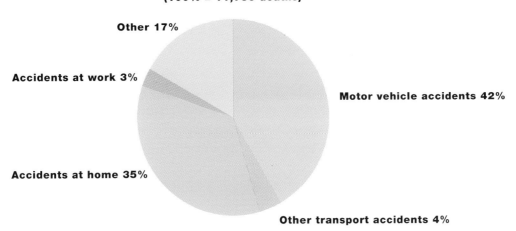

All Persons
(100% = 11,736 deaths)

Other 17%

Accidents at work 3%

Motor vehicle accidents 42%

Accidents at home 35%

Other transport accidents 4%

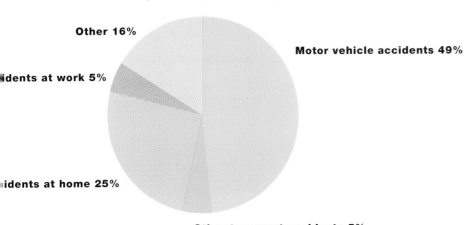

Males
(100% = 7,182 deaths)

Other 16%

idents at work 5%

Motor vehicle accidents 49%

idents at home 25%

Other transport accidents 5%

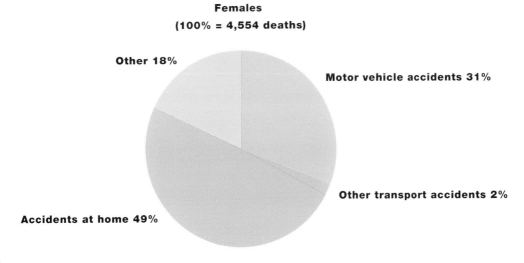

Females
(100% = 4,554 deaths)

Other 18%

Motor vehicle accidents 31%

Other transport accidents 2%

Accidents at home 49%

:e: OPCS (ICD E800:E949)

luding deaths at ages under 28 days   Percentages may not add up to 100 due to rounding

OBJECTIVE

To reduce ill-health, disability and death caused by accidents

TARGETS

E.5 Some targets already exist at national and international level for accident prevention, notably:

- the World Health Organisation target for a reduction by at least 25% in death from all types of accidents by the year 2000 from a 1980 baseline

- the Department of Transport target for a reduction in road casualties in Great Britain of one third by the year 2000 from a baseline of the average number of casualties in the years 1981 to 1985.

E.6 To build on these targets the Government has decided that there should be three national targets for accident prevention broken down by age to focus upon the groups most vulnerable to the risk of accidental injury – children, young people and elderly people. The targets are shown below and in *figure 19*.

A. **To reduce the death rate for accidents among children aged under 15 by at least 33% by 2005 (from 6.7 per 100,000 population in 1990 to no more than 4.5 per 100,000).**

B. **To reduce the death rate for accidents among young people aged 15–24 by at least 25% by 2005 (from 23.2 per 100,000 population in 1990 to no more than 17.4 per 100,000).**

C. **To reduce the death rate for accidents among people aged 65 and over by at least 33% by 2005 (from 56.7 per 100,000 population in 1990 to no more than 38 per 100,000).**

Figure 19

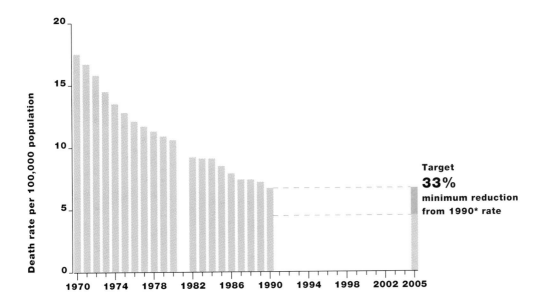

Death rates for Accidents

England 1970-1990*• and target for the year 2005

All persons aged under 15°

Source: OPCS (ICD E800:E949)

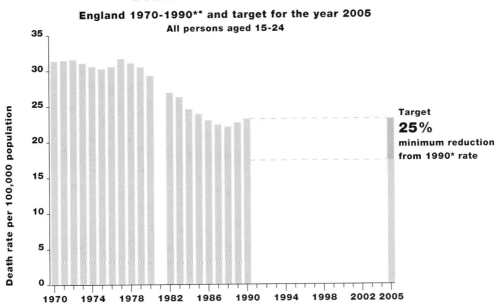

Death rates for Accidents

England 1970-1990*• and target for the year 2005

All persons aged 15-24

Source: OPCS (ICD E800:E949)

*Rates are calculated using a 3 year average plotted against the middle year of the average

•Data for 1981 were affected by industrial action by registrars and are excluded, thus rates for 1980 and 1982 are based on two year averages

°Rates are calculated using the European Standard Population to take into account differences in age structure

Figure 19 cont.

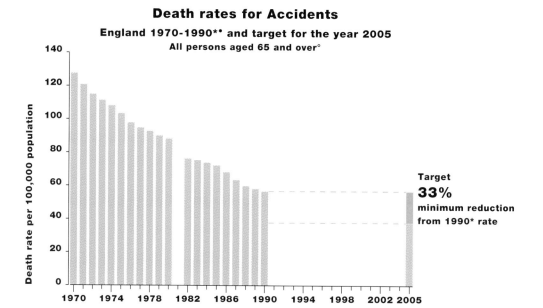

Death rates for Accidents

England 1970-1990** and target for the year 2005
All persons aged 65 and over°

Source: OPCS (ICD E800:E949)

*Rates are calculated using a 3 year average plotted against the middle year of the average
•Data for 1981 were affected by industrial action by registrars and are excluded, thus rates for 1980 and 1982 are based on two year averages
°Rates are calculated using the European Standard Population to take into account differences in age structure

E.7 Accident prevention is a complex undertaking with interests and responsibilities shared between individuals and their families, employers and a wide range of statutory and voluntary organisations at both national and local levels. In carrying forward these objectives, the Government will rely primarily on information and education and will avoid the imposition of unnecessary regulations on business and individuals.

• **National Government** sets standards, enacts and enforces legislation, provides guidance and allocated resources in support of accident prevention. **Local authorities**, with their various powers, have many opportunities to take safety considerations into account across virtually the whole range of the services they provide. The distribution of relevant interests between Government Departments is shown in *figure 20;* local authority involvement in accident prevention is summarised in *figure 21.*

Figure 20

GOVERNMENT INTERESTS IN ACCIDENT PREVENTION

DEPARTMENT FOR EDUCATION	**safety education and general health and safety matters (including accident prevention) in schools**
DEPARTMENT OF THE ENVIRONMENT	**safety aspects of town planning, building regulations and housing policies**
DEPARTMENT OF HEALTH	**(through the NHS) services to treat accidents and (with the HEA) the accident prevention element of health education**
HOME OFFICE	**fire safety and prevention of drowning accidents**
DEPARTMENT OF TRADE AND INDUSTRY	**safety of consumer goods and prevention of home accidents, safety of electricity lines and apparatus**
DEPARTMENT OF TRANSPORT	**road and transport safety**
THE HEALTH AND SAFETY COMMISSION AND EXECUTIVE	**reduction of risks to health and safety of workers and members of the public from work activity reporting to a number of Secretaries of State (principally Employment)**

These interests are shared with many other agencies and organisations. In a number of cases specific statutory responsibility lies with non-Governmental bodies.

- **Voluntary organisations** like the Royal Society for the Prevention of Accidents (RoSPA) and the Child Accident Prevention Trust (CAPT) have a very valuable advisory role and also undertake research, the production of education materials and promotional campaigns. There are also numerous community and voluntary groups, either with an interest in accident prevention among their objectives or formed specifically to address a particular hazard or safety issue.

- **Employers and trade unions** are concerned with health and safety at work.

Figure 21

LOCAL AUTHORITY INVOLVEMENT IN ACCIDENT PREVENTION

PLANNING	safety implications of planning, including the siting of new housing, play and recreation facilities and other amenities in relation to roads and provision for pedestrians and cyclists
BUILDING CONTROL	enforcement of the safety aspects of building regulations
HIGHWAYS	construction and maintenance of local authority roads, setting local casualty reduction targets, preparation of local road safety plans, accident investigation, design and implementation of local safety engineering schemes, road safety publicity and advice
HOUSING	home safety both through the design and maintenance of the local authority housing stock and the provision made for families and individuals requiring temporary accommodation
SOCIAL SERVICES	support services, including domiciliary and residential services, for vulnerable groups such as children, elderly people and people with disabilities. Social Service Department staff have similar opportunities to health professionals to advise on accident prevention and safety
EDUCATION	building and maintenance of schools and other maintained establishments, security, transport for schoolchildren and use of schools for leisure and recreational activities[1]
FIRE AND POLICE SERVICES	have both an emergency service and regulatory and advisory functions
ENVIRONMENTAL HEALTH AND CONSUMER PROTECTION	many local authorities employ specialist staff such as trading standards, road safety, home safety and environmental health officers who all contribute to accident prevention

[1] Under arrangements for the local management of schools and colleges, members of governing bodies now have responsibilities in this area.

E.8 The Government proposes to base its strategy around the following key elements:

- better co-ordination of agencies involved

- promotion of accident prevention as a public health issue

- better information

- action related to types of accidents

- action related to vulnerable groups.

- In addition to their role at the scene of accidents, the **emergency services** have an advisory and regulatory role.

- The **NHS** provides emergency services including ambulance services, hospital accident and emergency departments, trauma services, specialist intensive care units and rehabilitation services. It is also in a position to collect and use information about the results of accidents in drawing up prevention strategies. **The Health Education Authority's** national health promotion remit extends to the harm caused by accidents.

- **Primary health care teams and community child health doctors and other professionals in primary and secondary health care** are in regular contact with families with young children and can use these contacts to give advice on safety and accident prevention to the carers of young children. Many of these same professionals also have regular contacts with elderly people. Pharmacists give advice on the safe use, storage and disposal of medicines and on the dangers of driving or using machinery while taking certain medications. The Royal Pharmaceutical Society has set a professional requirement for community pharmacists to provide all solid oral dose preparations in child-resistant containers or in strip and blister packaging. Disposal of Unwanted Medicines and Poisons (DUMP) campaigns organised locally by health authorities and pharmacists remove old containers of medicines from homes and dispose of them safely with minimum damage to the environment.

(a) Co-ordination and Public Health

E.9 More effective co-ordination of the agencies involved in accident prevention at both national and local level would make a significant contribution to further reductions in accidents. **The Government therefore proposes to set up a task force to give a national lead on the accident prevention aspect of the health strategy.** Representatives from the relevant statutory and voluntary organisations will be invited to join this task force.

E.10 At local level the range of responsibilities and interests is equally wide. Both local authorities and District Health Authorities (DHAs) have key roles. Much of the action taken to achieve the targets will have implications for local authorities.

E.11 Many Directors of Public Health already include information about accidents in their reports on the health of the population in their District. The Government wishes to see Directors of Public Health provide a new focus for accident prevention through the collection of information about the impact of accidents on health and action which can be taken to reduce this toll. In doing this they will need to work closely with bodies with related responsibilities, particularly local authorities. **The Government will initiate discussions with Directors of Public Health to explore how their role in accident prevention can be developed.**

(b) Better information

E.12 It is generally accepted that accident prevention could be made more effective if better information were available which made clear the links between the causes and effects of accidents. The planning and monitoring of local accident prevention initiatives could be improved if it were possible to relate details of subsequent treatment and rehabilitation to the causes of the injuries treated in hospital accident and emergency departments. This might for example allow patterns or accident "blackspots" to be identified where straightforward action could be taken to reduce the problem. It would enable initiatives to be targeted on those areas offering most scope for improving the overall health of the local population. It would also help provide a fuller picture of the true cost of accidents which could be used to publicise the impact they have on the health and welfare in the local area.

E.13 The Government intends that improved information about numbers and types of accidents should be available locally, building upon the experience of the collection arrangements made in a sample of hospitals by the Department of Trade and Industry for its home and leisure accident surveillance systems. The growing use of computerised information systems in accident and emergency departments will facilitate this. **The aim is that all DHAs should have information about the cause and treatment of accidents among their resident populations** which can be used in local prevention initiatives including the setting of local targets for reducing the number of both fatal and non-fatal accidents.

(c) Road accidents

E.14 Enforcement of traffic law and increasing public respect for the law are important means of reducing accidents. The Road Traffic Act 1991 clarifies and strengthens this legislation by introducing, among other measures:

- a new extended driving test for drivers disqualified for dangerous driving

- the use of modern technology to detect speeding and traffic light offences

- a major experiment in the rehabilitation of drink–drive offenders

- provision for variable speed limits, eg in bad weather or outside schools at certain times of day.

E.15 Significant reductions in road casualties over the next 15 years could also be achieved by the promotion of safer vehicles. This will require agreement in the European Community on improved vehicle construction standards. The Government is already pressing for early agreement in Brussels. It will be necessary to reinforce these efforts, for example by enlisting the help of European medical opinion.

(d) Consumer and Home Safety

E.16 A prerequisite for a safe home environment is that the items in it should themselves be safe. The Department of Trade and Industry has lead responsibility for legislation here. Since the passing of the Consumer Safety Act in 1987, people have been able to sue for damages without having to establish negligence on the part of the manufacturer. It is a criminal offence to supply unsafe goods. Last year a General Product Safety Directive was agreed in the EC which will eventually require other Community countries to introduce a similar safeguard. The Government has also brought into United Kingdom law a number of EC directives which must be met by a wide range of products including toys and electrical appliances. Trading standards officers employed by local authorities are responsible for the enforcement of consumer safety legislation and by doing so make an important contribution to accident prevention.

E.17 The Department complements its legislative and regulatory role on consumer safety with a wide range of promotional campaigns aimed at informing people about home safety issues. These include annual fireworks and Christmas toy safety campaigns as well as one-off campaigns, often run in collaboration with voluntary bodies or the private sector.

E.18 Revised building regulations will come into force this year. These include improved fire, structural and stair safety together with a new requirement for safe glazing. Regulations are also to be introduced this year governing the storage of hazardous substances. Each year the Home Office, in conjunction with the Fire Protection Association, organises National Fire Safety Week. It acts as a focus to attract the support of the insurance industry, commercial organisations, manufacturers and retailers of fire safety equipment and voluntary organisations in helping to promote the fire-safety message to the public.

(e) Accidents in the workplace

E.19 Employers have the primary responsibility for ensuring safety in the workplace, both for their employees and for others who may be affected by their activities. At national level, the Health and Safety Commission and Executive will be carrying forward a major legislative programme as well as considering new approaches to enforcement advice and assistance. Forthcoming legislation will include:

- new general requirements for systematic assessment and management of health and safety risks by all employers

- new health and safety requirements covering construction sites and the offshore oil and gas industry

- regulations on the manual handling of loads, which account for one third of all reported accidents at work.

E.20 Operation and enforcement will include campaigns in high accident sectors such as agriculture and construction. Particular emphasis will be put on improving the ability of employers and others to systematically manage and assess risks to health and safety.

(f) Vulnerable groups – children, elderly people and people with disabilities

E.21 Those most vulnerable to accidents include children, elderly people and people with disabilities, all of whom to varying degrees may be reliant upon others for their safety. These might be parents, relatives or carers from the immediate community, a voluntary organisation or a statutory body in the health or social services. For people reliant on others, good quality care and supervision may be the best protection from harm and much of the work of external agencies is to support carers looking after people vulnerable to accidents. Schemes for the loan of items like fire or stair guards, car seat restraints or aids to everyday living are examples of the support provided locally.

E.22 The Government supports activities designed to help more vulnerable people guard themselves against accidents. It collaborated with the Child Accident Prevention Trust and the BBC on a nationwide child safety campaign aimed at maximising the effect of the "Play It Safe" television documentaries broadcast earlier this year. Already available are materials for use in mounting local child accident prevention programmes and a training resource for health visitors.

E.23 The Department of Transport is engaged in an extensive road safety campaign and is working closely with other Departments, local authorities and voluntary organisations to improve child road safety. This includes major publicity campaigns aimed at parents and drivers. The involvement of the private sector has been encouraged at both national and local level, a partnership which the Government will be seeking to extend and encourage in other fields of accident prevention.

E.24 The Home Office has targeted national television advertising promoting smoke alarm ownership at elderly people and their carers. In 1989 and 1990 a Mobile Unit for the elderly was set up with Age Concern. It toured major urban retail market areas taking the fire safety message to elderly people. It also served to encourage closer co-operation between local fire brigades, Age Concern and other local groups. The Department of Transport has issued a policy document – "The Older Road User" – which summarises the road safety problems faced by elderly people as drivers, pedestrians and bus passengers and identifies a range of measures for reducing casualties.

E.25 As falls are a particularly important cause of accidents amongst older people, the Department of Health will be considering what research might be commissioned into the prevention of falls in elderly people.

VARIATIONS

E.26 As with other conditions there are variations in rates of accidental injuries, which have implications for policy development both nationally and locally. Twice as many boys as girls die from accidents and children of both sexes from economically deprived backgrounds have the highest rates of accidental deaths. Children of low income families – especially those living in temporary accommodation – have been identified as being at particular risk. Research is continuing into the relationship between children's risk of accidental injury and their membership of an ethnic minority group. Current evidence is inconclusive on this, but accident prevention initiatives need to be tailored to meet and take full advantage of the circumstances of specific groups.

CONSEQUENTIAL IMPROVEMENTS IN HEALTH

E.27 Accidents contribute to a very significant amount of ill-health and disability, which in some cases may be life-long. As more information becomes available about the consequences of accidents, it will be possible to make better estimates of the level of chronic illness and disability that could be avoided.

SECTION F

KEY AREAS AND THE HEALTH OF PEOPLE IN SPECIFIC GROUPS OF THE POPULATION

INTRODUCTION

F.1 When framing action in the Key Areas – and more generally – it will be necessary to consider the particular needs and concerns of specific groups of people within the population. In other words, the issues addressed by Key Areas and targets need to be disaggregated further to ensure coverage of the whole population, not just parts of it.

HEALTH OF INFANTS AND CHILDREN

F.2 All the Key Areas are relevant to the health of infants and children at all stages from birth to adolescence. In some cases, success in meeting targets in Key Areas will have consequential benefits for infants and children – for example reducing cases of low birthweight associated with expectant mothers smoking during pregnancy. In other cases, success with children – for example in establishing healthy lifestyles at a young age – will itself be crucial to the long-term success of the strategy.

F.3 *Figure 22* summarises the implications of the Key Areas for the health of infants and children.

HEALTH OF ELDERLY PEOPLE

F.4 Similarly, all the Key Areas are relevant to elderly people. In 1990, 13% of men and 18% of women were aged 65 years or over. The number of very elderly people will increase in the next decade, with those aged 85 years and over expected to increase by 34%. Their needs will become an increasingly important factor in programmes designed to safeguard and improve the health of the population. Of particular note is the fact that in many cases preventive measures can be just as successful in elderly men and women as in younger people.

INFANTS AND CHILDREN

Figure 22

CORONARY HEART DISEASE AND STROKE	The maintenance of healthy lifestyles such as balanced diet and exercise in adulthood is more likely if established during childhood. The adoption of healthy lifestyles during childhood encourages optimum growth and resistance to ill-health, both emotional and physical. There is increasing evidence to suggest that there is a relationship between growth and development starting from before birth and during childhood, and risk in later life of CHD, raised blood pressure and other risk factors.
CANCERS	Cancers are an important cause of illness and death in childhood, though the causes of most childhood cancers are not well understood. Approximately 80% of adult smokers started smoking as teenagers. Action to reduce smoking amongst teenagers is therefore crucial to reducing subsequent smoking in adult life. Reduction of smoking during pregnancy will reduce the risk of low birthweight, and stillbirth and death in infancy. Reduction of parental smoking will reduce the prevalence during infancy of respiratory disease, and possibly the risk of chronic ear infections. There may also be a link with sudden infant death. Children of non-smoking parents are less likely to start smoking.
MENTAL ILLNESS	Child and adolescent psychiatric and psychological services have a leading role in promoting the psychological health and well-being of children and adolescents. There is increasing evidence that early effective intervention in childhood and adolescence can be important in preventing adult mental ill-health. The impaired mental health of adults can also have an adverse impact on their children's health, both emotional and physical.
HIV/AIDS AND SEXUAL HEALTH	Access to effective family planning services can promote child and family health by enabling preconception care to be instituted and pregnancies to be planned and spaced. Reduction in the prevalence of HIV in women of childbearing age will reduce the number of babies born with HIV. Active sexual life often begins during adolescence, and the adoption of responsible and healthy sexual lifestyles should be promoted at this time.
ACCIDENTS	Accidents are the leading cause of death amongst children and young people. The consequences of some accidents can be life-long disability or a predisposition to ill-health later in life. Action to reduce accidents will have a significant effect on the health and well-being of children.

F.5 *Figure 23* relates the Key Areas to the health of elderly people.

ELDERLY PEOPLE

Figure 23

CORONARY HEART DISEASE AND STROKE	CHD and stroke are major causes of ill-health and mortality in elderly people. The risk of both increases with age. The risk factors for CHD and stroke in old age are the same as those in middle age, and adopting a healthy lifestyle even late in life is beneficial (although ideally healthy living should start in youth and continue. Healthy lifestyles help prevent other ill-health). For example, physical activity not only helps prevent CHD, but can also help prevent other disorders such as osteoporosis. It is not however possible to prevent all cases of CHD and stroke. Effective treatment and rehabilitation services will continue to be vital for the health of elderly people.
CANCERS	Many of the people who suffer from cancers are elderly, because the risk of many types of cancer increases with age. In men over 65 the most frequently diagnosed new cases of cancer are cancer of the lung, trachea or bronchus, while amongst women breast cancer is the most frequent cancer, although lung cancer is increasing. Giving up smoking is just as important in preventing lung cancer in elderly people as in the young. Women over 65 may continue to be screened every three years for breast cancer if they request it.
MENTAL ILLNESS	The prevalence of most types of mental illness is just as high amongst elderly people as in the population as a whole. However, depression, suicide and dementia are more common and problems associated with bereavement and isolation increase. There may be opportunities to prevent the dementia caused by cerebrovascular disease, but the treatment of Alzheimer's dementia relies on the appropriate and effective combination of health and supportive social services.
HIV/AIDS AND SEXUAL HEALTH	Older people can enjoy sexual relations just as much as younger people, but equally may need medical help and advice should difficulties occur.
ACCIDENTS	Accidents are an important cause of ill-health and death in elderly people. 70% of all fatal home accidents occur in people aged 65 and over, and more than 300,000 people over 65 attend accident and emergency departments each year as a result of a home accident. Falls account for 65% of these. Reducing accidents will have a major impact on the health and well-being of elderly people.

HEALTH OF WOMEN

F.6 The particular health needs of women should be considered in addressing Key Areas. Although the targets and approach to improving the nation's health set out in this document apply to both men and women, a number of diseases are specific to, or chiefly found in, women. In addition, patterns of disease and death can and do vary between men and women.

F.7 In general, women are healthier and live longer than ever before. Nevertheless, they have specific health needs and problems. As well as health issues relating to pregnancy and childbirth, only women develop cancer of the cervix or womb, or experience severe, even incapacitating, premenstrual and menopausal symptoms. Some conditions (eg osteoporosis and cystitis) chiefly affect women. It is because of this that women's health has been a priority in recent years.

F.8 In the Key Area of cancer, specific targets have been set to reduce deaths amongst women from breast and cervical cancers. In addition to that, health authorities should pay regard to gender differences in patterns of ill-health in developing local action to achieve targets. For example, in 1991 lung cancer was the most common cause of cancer death in men (31% of cancer deaths) and accounted for 16% of cancer deaths in women; breast cancer was the most common cause of cancer death in women (20%). Although more men die from coronary heart disease than women, the male death rate from coronary heart disease is falling faster.

F.9 The UK was the first country in the European Community and amongst the first in the world to introduce national population breast and cervical cancer screening programmes based on inviting women by computerised call and recall. In addition, the Government has a number of initiatives and projects aimed at improving the health of women, including:

- research into menopause and osteoporosis including analysis of the costs and benefits of hormone replacement therapy and evaluating techniques for osteoporosis screening;

- a well-received and widely available booklet, published in June 1991, detailing services available to women in the NHS and voluntary sector;

- the national programme on smoking and pregnancy will continue; developing proposals for a major health education programme on smoking aimed at adults will focus on groups at particular risk such as young adult women.

F.10 Good quality family planning and maternity services are essential to women. Initiatives to maintain and improve services are set out in the *appendix* (Section D). In particular, the Confidential Enquiry into Stillbirth and Deaths in Infancy launched in 1991 is intended to reduce further the incidence of these tragic events. Improving family planning services is a high priority for the NHS. It is important that women know what is available so that they and their partners can make informed choices.

HEALTH OF PEOPLE FROM BLACK AND ETHNIC MINORITY GROUPS

F.11 The needs of people from black and ethnic minority groups likewise need to be considered in addressing Key Areas. Rates of ill-health and death amongst black and ethnic minority groups show differences to those for the white population and between individual ethnic minority groups for all of the Key Areas.

F.12 For example, death rates for coronary heart disease are higher than the white population in people (especially women) who have originated from the Indian sub-continent, but lower in those from the Caribbean. On the other hand this latter group has higher rates of stroke. Smoking prevalence is lower than the white population in people of Afro-Caribbean and Asian origin. There are however other minority groups – eg people from Turkey – where rates are higher. The HIV educational and health needs of black and ethnic minority groups also must be addressed, including those infected abroad.

F.13 Local decisions about action to achieve targets will need to take account of the particular needs of people from black and ethnic minority groups. It will be necessary to consider both the implications of these differences for overall strategies and also to ensure that the specific needs of people in black and ethnic minority groups are targeted. For example, information produced for black and ethnic minority groups needs to be culturally and linguistically sensitive.

F.14 At national level, the Government is supporting a variety of projects aimed at increasing understanding of the specific needs of people in black and ethnic minority groups, and of the ways in which these can be met. For example it has funded:

- the Royal Society for the Prevention of Accidents (RoSPA) to identify good practice on the coverage of child accident prevention in health promotion campaigns among black and ethnic minority groups;

- the Aga Khan Foundation to undertake an analysis of Asian foods to help formulate accurate and relevant advice to the Asian population on diet;

- Yorkshire RHA to run a pilot project to improve uptake of cervical and breast cancer screening among women from black and ethnic minority groups;

- the Maudsley Outreach Support and Treatment Team to produce a video designed to raise awareness amongst people in black and ethnic minority groups of the range of psychiatric services in this country;

- the Institute of Psychiatry to look at the long-term outcome of psychosis in Afro-Caribbean people.

The Ministerially-led AIDS Action Group includes in its remit dissemination of good practice on the provison of HIV-related services in ways which take account of the needs of black and ethnic minority groups.

SOCIO-ECONOMIC GROUPS

F.15 In England, as in all other westernised countries, there are variations in health status between different socio-economic groups within the population.

F.16 In general, people in manual occupational groups (and therefore social classes IIIM, IV and V) have higher rates of illness and death than those in non-manual groups (social classes I, II and IIIN). With very few exceptions (eg breast cancer) death rates from the leading causes of death are higher in manual groups, though there are marked variations even within each group. This pattern appears to hold for all the Key Areas, though hard evidence is not so readily available for non-fatal conditions, nor for HIV.

F.17 The reasons for these variations are by no means fully understood. They are likely to be the result of a complex interplay of genetic, biological, social, environmental, cultural and behavioural factors.

F.18 In part they are accounted for by differences in risk behaviour. People in manual groups are, for example, more likely to smoke, and to eat diets containing less vitamin C and ß-carotene. There is also a higher proportion of heavy drinkers in manual than non-manual groups (though on the other hand there is also a higher proportion of people who never drink, or who drink only very lightly and infrequently). There is also evidence of lower take-up of preventive health services (eg immunisation, child health surveillance) in groups whose health is worst.

F.19 The different needs of people in different socio-economic groups will need to be considered in framing action in Key Areas. Sometimes action can be at a national level. National mass media health education could be targeted on groups at particular risk. There will be an important national role in ensuring that research continues to elucidate the reasons for these differences.

F.20 At local level, attention needs to be paid to responding to particular needs. In many cases, much could be achieved by simple measures such as changing the presentation, description and opening times of services to be relevant to the circumstances and perceptions of users and potential users.

PEOPLE WITH PHYSICAL OR SENSORY DISABILITIES OR LEARNING DISABILITIES

F.21 Special consideration will need to be given to people with physical disabilities, sensory impairments or learning disabilities in two separate ways when implementing action in Key Areas. First, some conditions or risks may apply in particular ways to them and may need special solutions. In the case of accidents in the home, for example, people with disabilities may be at greater than average risk. Secondly, care and special provision will be needed to ensure that health promotion messages and other information are adequately and conveniently made accessible to people in these groups.

OTHER GROUPS

F.22 Similarly, account will need to be taken of the special problems which face people in other groups, such as unpaid part- or full-time carers and the homeless.

F.23 It is also important to note that there are significant variations in health, and in the prevalence of risk factors, between different parts of the country, not all of which can be fully accounted for by other known factors such as socio-economic groupings or ethnicity.

TECHNICAL NOTES ON TARGET SETTING AND MONITORING

Target setting

1 Targets have been set in this document for a wide variety of factors pertaining to the health status of the population, including targets for mortality (eg CHD, stroke, accidents), morbidity (eg incidence of cervical cancer), precursors of disease (eg high blood pressure) and behaviours which can influence disease risk (eg cigarette and alcohol consumption). The process of target setting has varied from target to target according to the quantity and quality of information currently available, the potential to monitor progress, and knowledge concerning the availability, effectiveness and likely impact of interventions.

2 The underlying aim has been to identify in each case a target which is challenging yet achievable. The first stage of this process is therefore to try to assess what will happen in the future if no *additional* action is taken. However, incomplete knowledge of *all* factors affecting changes in the incidence of diseases and their determinants generally precludes refined assessments of future trends. While assessment of the effects of, and interactions between key variables (eg risk factors for CHD) can be informed by such methods as computer modelling, there is a danger of creating a spurious sense of accuracy if such approaches are used to add detail rather than to increase the scope and coherence of assessments. However, using available information, an estimate must be made of likely future trends and then combined with an assessment of the *potential* impact of successfully implemented interventions in order to produce a challenging yet achievable target.

3 For the reasons given, target setting must be based on a combination of science and informed judgement. The balance between these two will vary from target to target as will the extent to which the targets chosen are aspirational rather than precise measures of what should happen if available interventions are successfully applied.

4 Some of the factors considered in the setting of the CHD mortality reduction target are outlined here as an example of the process.

    (a)   Review of recent mortality trends in England
- age-specific rates
- age-standardised rates

    (b)   Extrapolation of past trends to produce projections
- based on 1981–1990 trend
- based on 1986–1990 trend

    (c)   Birth cohort analysis of mortality trends

    (d)   International data
- current mortality rates
- mortality reductions achieved in USA, Australia and European Community countries (both absolute and percentage reductions)
- review of targets proposed in other national exercises

    (e)   Possible effects of current and future interventions

    (f)   Review of recommendations made by various experts.

Monitoring

5 The diversity of targets presented in this document dictate a similarly wide variety of means of monitoring progress. Thus sources will include mortality statistics, cancer registration data, Korner aggregate returns and the new health survey programme for England. It is important that the monitoring parameters are made explicit to enable, wherever possible, national and local monitoring to share a common basis. The Department of Health will therefore publish in due course a detailed appraisal of information and indicators needed to monitor progress in each Key Area.

Age adjustment

6 In order to allow for changes in the age structure of the population over time, mortality rates – and, where appropriate, morbidity rates – are standardised to the European standard population in the appropriate age ranges. The European standard population is as published in the World Health Statistics Annual (WHO, Geneva).

Baseline year

7 In most cases, the selected baseline year is 1990. Where 1990 data are unavailable, the most up-to-date available data has been selected. The baseline figure for the mortality targets for CHD, stroke, breast cancer, suicide and accidents represents an average of three years centred around 1990. The 1991 rates are calculated using provisional estimates for the mid-1991 population. In due course use of 1991 census-based population estimates may result in minor adjustments to the baseline rates presented in this document.

Target year

8 In most cases the selected target year is the year 2000. This has the advantage of being compatible with the WHO Health for All by the year 2000 initiative and provides sufficient time for interventions to produce an effect. For a few targets a more distant target year has been selected because of the estimated time lag for interventions to be implemented and to achieve their effect and for changes to be monitored. A small number of targets have been set for achievement earlier than the year 2000.

Geographical areas

9 Wherever possible the statistics quoted in this document, the baselines and the targets relate to England. For some topics the data have been collected or analysed in such a way that it was not practical to extract data for England only. In these cases the statistics used relate to the smallest appropriate geographical area for which data were available, and for monitoring it will be necessary to ensure that data are consistent with the baseline.

PREPARED BY THE DEPARTMENT OF HEALTH AND
PRINTED IN THE UK FOR HMSO Dd0509797 2/93 C50 51-1135